SOLAR ELECTRICITY:
Making The Sun Work For You

Written by the technical staff of MONEGON, Ltd.

SOLAR ELECTRICITY:
Making The Sun Work For You

PRINCIPAL AUTHORS:	Charles E. Bullock
	Peter H. Grambs
CONTRIBUTING AUTHORS:	Douglas A. Ames
	Scott C. Kaufman
SENIOR EDITOR:	Dr. H.L. Macomber
CONSULTING EDITOR:	Dr. Jean D. Grambs
EDITORS:	Charles E. Bullock
	Peter H. Grambs
PROJECT COORDINATOR:	Charles E. Bullock
PRODUCTION:	Ellen M. Tanzi
GRAPHIC ARTIST:	Jeanie D. Eisenberg
COVER PHOTO:	Theresa A. Twilley

COPYRIGHT © MONEGON, LTD. 1981

International Standard Book Number: 0-940520-00-1
Library of Congress Catalog Card Number: 81-82421

Printed and bound in the United States of America.

Table of Contents

Preface

Photovoltaics? Some people know what it means, some know how to pronounce it, but only a few people fully understand the field. Yet the use of "solar electric" power systems is increasing rapidly and the potential exists for the extensive worldwide use of solar electric power systems in the near future.

Until recently, most sources of energy were in relatively unrestricted and inexpensive abundance. Yet within the last ten years, it has become apparent that many of our current sources of usable energy (e.g. natural gas, oil, and nuclear fission) at current consumption and inflation rates, will be either depleted or very costly in the foreseeable future.

This increased awareness of energy issues has been forced upon us by such problems as the harmful effects of oil supply interruptions on the economy, rapid price increases and their effect on our standards of living, and environmental difficulties resulting from the operation of power generating plants. This awareness of the importance of adequate and secure supplies of energy has in turn expanded interest in alternatives to our current dependence upon fossil fuels and nuclear energy resources. These alternatives are receiving close scrutiny as a means to reduce both excessive use of energy and our dependence upon these increasingly expensive nonrenewable energy resources. In addition to energy conservation efforts, solar energy appears to be the most promising renewable energy resource.

Although currently there are many useful solar technologies, the generation of electricity directly from solar energy is particularly attractive, since a significant portion of worldwide energy use is in the form of electricity. The direct conversion of solar energy to electricity, or the generation of "solar electricity," is called "photovoltaics." Photovoltaics is a well-established technology which many energy experts believe has the potential to satisfy a large part of our energy needs in the future. Photovoltaics will provide electricity from abundant, inexhaustible, and free solar energy to operate everything from appliances and vehicles to entire towns and cities.

Yet while solar electric power systems have been used successfully around the world for years, few people know of these uses or understand the principles behind the generation of solar electricity. Realizing the current opportunities and the future potential for the use of solar electricity, the technical staff at MONEGON, Ltd. conceived of this book as a means of acquainting you with the basics of photovoltaics. We believe that only through an understanding of all our energy resources can we determine which of the many energy options should be used in the future.

This book is intended to provide the reader with a basic understanding of solar electricity. In writing this book, we believe that these power systems will begin to be in common use in the next several years. Consequently, there is no better time than the present to become familiar with photovoltaics technology, and the effect of widespread use of this energy source on your future.

MONEGON, Ltd.
June, 1981

CHAPTER 1

Prologue To A Solar Future

Introduction

Imagine walking down a street on a bright spring day. There is a chill in the air as you walk along the straight, well-kept avenues of this small city. Here and there you can spot a plume of smoke rising from a cozy fire in someone's home. But you do not see many of the telltale signs of warming fires; there is a shortage of firewood. You notice that all of the homes are built with a southern exposure and catch the full strength of the sun's rays. On the roofs of some of these homes you notice some interesting objects. You recognize them as devices used to heat water for the house, using only the energy of the sun to operate. They appear to be simple, yet obviously functional additions to the home.

Smelling a sweet fragrance in the air, and looking around, you notice that many of the homes are landscaped with trees that are in blossom, with new leaves just beginning to take shape. These trees are not located at random. They seem to be placed carefully in order to provide shade in the hot summer months. In the winter the leafless branches allow the sun's warming rays to enter the buildings.

As you continue your journey through this pleasant city, you peek into an open doorway. You see a home built around an open courtyard filled with plants of innumerable shape, size, and color. On the roof on one side of the courtyard is what appears to be cloth, or some other light material, which is rolled into a bundle. When you inquire about this, you are told that it is a covering for the courtyard. The covering is removed on sunny days to let the full strength of the sun shine down into the garden. At

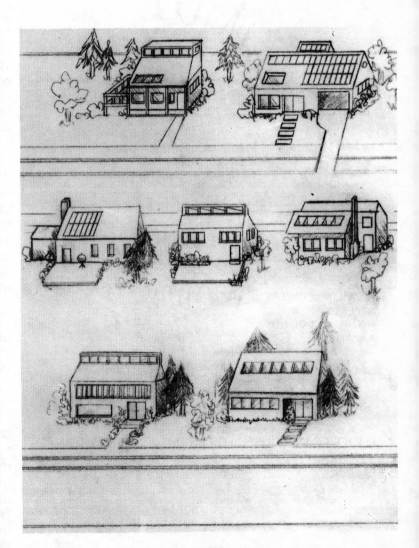

A SOLAR COMMUNITY

WINTER HEATING

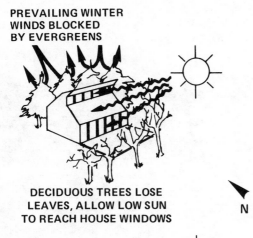

PREVAILING WINTER
WINDS BLOCKED
BY EVERGREENS

DECIDUOUS TREES LOSE
LEAVES, ALLOW LOW SUN
TO REACH HOUSE WINDOWS

N

SUMMER COOLING

PREVAILING SUMMER
BREEZES PROVIDE
NATURAL COOLING

DECIDUOUS TREES
POSITIONED TO
SHADE PATIO, HOUSE

TREES CAN BE USED FOR ENERGY CONSERVATION

night, or on rainy days, the cloth can be used to protect the plants, yet let the sunlight in, creating the effect of a greenhouse in the middle of the house.

You are now entering what looks to be the commercial district of the city. You notice the same type of architecture here as you saw in the homes; southern exposure with trees carefully placed. The stores seem to be located in such a manner that the solar water heating devices which they also have, are not shadowed by any other building. You learn that the law in this city explicitly requires that the sun rights of a building be protected from the shadows of other buildings.

There is a bustle of activity around you; fast moving vehicles travelling down the street, an office building being built to your left, some type of manufacturing activity taking place down the road. But with all this activity the air is clear; there is none of the sulphurous odors which normally are associated with the daily life of a city. That sweet, crisp fragrance of blossoming trees is a pleasure to your senses.

As you have taken this short journey through our imaginary city, what have been your thoughts? Is this a model solar community of the year 2000? Perhaps. While it may be the city of the future, it is also the description of a small Roman city, over two thousand years ago. Down through early modern history, in China, in Greece, in Rome, in Africa, and in the other cradles of civilization throughout the world, solar architecture, and the related use of the sun's energy for heat and power have been common.

But in the many years since this little city flourished in the sun, people have all but forgotten the many ways the sun can help in daily life. At first, the abundant forests of the continents were cut down to provide heat and power. Then, as this great resource diminished, coal deposits were explored, and their wealth exploited. But coal was not enough to satisfy technology's great thirst for energy. Oil and gas were discovered, and became the power sources of the world. Then the nuclear age dawned, bringing with it seemingly inexhaustable energy. But we are rapidly using up the world's oil resources, and nuclear energy is a debatable replacement, not only for safety reasons, but because of its ever increasing cost.

As we are once more returning to what the Romans knew in our quest for a dependable, safe, and clean source of energy, we are rediscovering the power of the sun. Many people believe that solar power can make a major contribution to the world's energy needs in the decades ahead. There are a number of solar technologies, from passive solar architecture to solar water heating and space heating and cooling. But the technology which may have the greatest potential to contribute to our energy supplies is the direct conversion of sunlight to electricity. This technology is called "photovoltaics."*

Photovoltaic power systems are virtually maintenance-free, have no inherent limit to their lifetime, cause no pollution when operating, and in the not-too-distant future will supply cheap electricity to individual homes, to offices, to schools, and to any other location with sunlight. Photovoltaics are not the total answer to our energy needs, but electricity generated from the sun can help us end our dependence on scarce or expensive sources of energy, and assist us in our persistent need for the energy to power civilization.

SOURCES OF ENERGY FOR THE U.S. IN 1981

---

*Since photovoltaics is a cumbersome term, many people refer to photovoltaics as "PV."

This book was written to give the reader a basic understanding of photovoltaics. We believe photovoltaics will be an important source of energy throughout the world in the years ahead. After reading our book, you will be on your way to understanding how photovoltaics will help you.

Many people who have heard about photovoltaics still believe that it is an "exotic" power source; Chapter 2 illustrates the many ways around the world by which photovoltaics already are being used, and it will dispel any myths about the exotic nature of solar electricity. Chapter 3 is designed to acquaint you with solar energy and its measurement. In Chapter 4 of this book, you will find a discussion of how photovoltaic arrays work, and of what they are composed. Chapter 5 describes the different parts of a photovoltaic system and their functions, while Chapter 6 introduces photovoltaic system design concepts. For those readers who are thinking about purchasing their own photovoltaic system for their home, cabin, or a host of other uses, Chapters 7 and 8 detail the many ways that the Federal and State governments might help you through tax credits, incentive programs, building codes, and the law.

Many of you, as you read this book, may become interested in business, employment, or educational opportunities in photovoltaics; Chapter 9 is for you. And for those with an eye toward the future, Chapter 10 offers a look at the contribution of photovoltaics to the United States and to the world in the coming decades.

The Quest for Energy

Throughout history, we have used many different forms of energy. In prehistoric times, human beings relied on their own muscles for the energy needed to exist. As nomadic life gave way to more permanent settlements, animals were domesticated and used to supplement human power. But with the discovery of fire, it became possible to harness the world's vast natural resources to provide the energy necessary for settled societies and eventually for whole civilizations.

Wood and other "bio-resources" such as peat, woody plants, and animal manure, have been used for energy for thousands of years around the globe. In many developing countries, these "traditional fuels" as they are called, are still one of the major energy sources, and may account for 90 percent or more of the energy used. It has been estimated that over half of the present world population relies on these simple bio-resources for some or all of their heating and cooking needs!

Although many people still count on bio-resources for their energy needs, the energy supplied by these sources is no longer a significant portion of world energy use. The wood resources of the industrialized countries have diminished dramatically in the last hundred years or so, and wood is no longer used to supply major amounts of energy. In the United States, for instance, wood was practically the sole fuel used by the early colonists. When settlers began to arrive in the New World in the early 17th century, they came to a continent which was heavily wooded from coast to coast. The colonists used wood for fuel, to build homes, wagons, and ships, or just cleared the forests in order to plant crops.

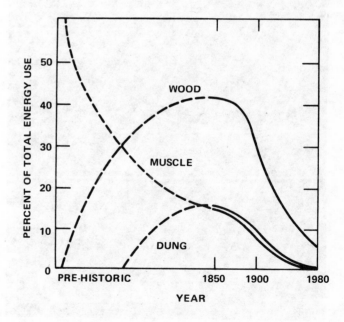

USE OF TRADITIONAL ENERGY SOURCES HAS DECLINED

But over the past several hundred years, as our population grew at a feverish pace, more and more land was cleared for bigger cities and more crop land, and wood was used to fuel this growth. As our forest resources dwindled, a new energy source, coal, was discovered in abundance.

In the United States, coal had been mined as early as 1701, in Richmond, Virginia. In other parts of the world, it had been mined in small quantities for centuries. Between 1830 and 1930, a transition occurred, from the use of wood to the use of coal as the primary energy source. New industrial processes developed that cannot use wood effectively as the source of energy.

The "Industrial Revolution" swept over most of Europe and North America during the 1800's. New industrial technologies, such as the Bessemer steel making process, the Siemen's regenerative furnace, the steam engine and other innovations exploited the chemical and physical characteristics of coal to provide increased rates of production at lower prices.

The emerging steel industry, railways, and production line manufacturing industries used coal throughout their operations; they did not just rely on it as a substitute for fuel wood. With this increasing industrialization arose an unprecedented demand for coal. Our forefathers probably concluded that they had found the ideal energy source.

COAL AWAITING DELIVERY

Petroleum and the 20th Century

Coal did not remain as the predominate source of energy for many years. There was a lot of it around, but as the surface mines close to the the industrial centers were exhausted, it became harder and more costly to mine and transport. And a ready substitute that was cheap and easy to obtain was in ever increasing supply—petroleum.

When oil was first discovered by a retired railroad conductor by the name of Edwin Drake in the State of Pennsylvania in 1859, it heralded the beginning of the oil age. The use of coal did not decline greatly, but as demand for energy increased rapidly in the early 20th century it was met by petroleum. After World War I, use of oil soared, as new and larger deposits were discovered. Oil was cheap; it was abundant; and it was ideally suited to industrial processes and transportation. In fact, it was perfect for use in the internal combustion engine which was being used in the new, personal form of transportation, called the automobile.

In the United States, World War II was accompanied by an explosion of industrial growth, population growth, and consequent growth in the Gross National Product. The automobile was catching on like wildfire; in 1930, there were 23 million motorcars on the nation's roads, by 1960, there were over 60 million. This growth demanded energy in seemingly unlimited quantities, and oil supplied more and more of the power needed.

In 1925, world consumption of oil was under 970 million barrels each year, but by 1970, we were consuming over 16 billion barrels of oil (each barrel contains 42 gallons) annually! In 1970, the United States consumed over 35 percent of this world

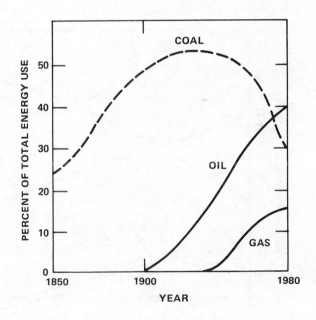

THE USE OF OIL AND GAS
HAS RISEN SINCE 1900

total. To give you an idea of how much oil this is, if all of the petroleum used in the world in 1970 was in barrels four and a half feet tall, and these barrels were stacked, they would stretch from the earth to the moon almost 60 times! But no one worried about this huge use of the earth's resources, for again everyone believed that we had found an almost inexhaustable supply of energy. Besides, nuclear power had come of age.

In 1945, the results of the Manhattan Project heralded the dawn of nuclear power with devastating suddenness when the first atomic bomb was dropped on Hiroshima. The immense power of atomic fission was harnessed in the first nuclear electricity generating plant in 1951. Industrialized countries, and developing countries, rushed to build nuclear power plants to power growing economies. Between 1951 and 1978, over 220 nuclear power plants were built around the globe. Once again, we believed that our unquenchable demand for energy would forever be satisfied by a combination of oil and nuclear energy resources. But in the 1970's, this belief was shattered.

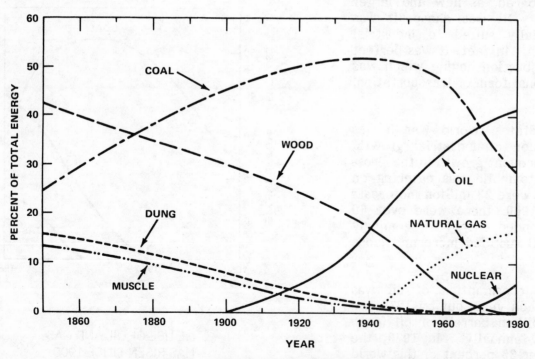

AN HISTORICAL LOOK AT ENERGY CONSUMPTION

The Oil Embargo and Three Mile Island — A Turning Point

In 1973, a little known group of oil producing nations, called the Organization of Petroleum Exporting Countries, embargoed shipments of oil to the United States, Europe and Japan. This organization, now known around the world as OPEC, escalated the price of their oil, and came close to bringing the industrialized world to a standstill. Petroleum that cost about $1.20 a barrel in the Persian Gulf in 1969, sold for $10 in 1975. Suddenly, oil could no longer be taken for granted.

Since 1973, the price of oil has risen at a dramatic pace. As of this writing, a barrel of oil costs over $32, and gasoline is selling for close to $1.40 a gallon in the United States, and over $3.00 in some European countries. We have come to realize that we are dangerously dependent upon imported oil for a large portion of our energy. As the upheaval in Iran in the past several years and the ongoing war between Iraq and Iran have clearly demonstrated, there is only a fragile stability to the world oil market. Few people who were driving cars in 1973 or 1978 will forget the lines of cars waiting to buy gasoline, nor will owners of oil heated homes forget the massive cost to heat their homes in the past few years. Oil is no longer cheap, and at the current worldwide rate of consumption, it will not be abundant within 20 years.

When the oil embargo hit, many people thought nuclear power would provide for our energy needs. But the crisis at Three Mile Island in 1979, and its implications for potential disaster radically altered these perceptions. Even before this event, the cost and construction time for nuclear plants had been rising so quickly that large facilities were rapidly

REMEMBER THE GAS LINES?

becoming prohibitively expensive and time consuming. The potential danger of a nuclear plant and the high cost has forced a reassessment of our energy needs and the means to meet these needs. A return to coal has been proposed, yet the pollution, the environmental problems, the uncertainty induced by labor trouble and the cost associated with coal mining and coal powered generating plants has raised serious questions concerning the acceptability of this approach.

Since the days of Rome, new energy sources have been sought and developed, each with its own advantages, limitations and hazards. The sources which now provide most of the world's energy, petroleum, natural gas, coal, and nuclear power are plagued with problems, many of which cannot be easily resolved. In the view of many, after an intermission of 2000 years, it is time again to turn to the sun. To be sure, solar energy is not the complete answer to our energy problems. But it is an energy source which can help meet our energy needs. It deserves our attention.

Solar Energy — An Ancient Solution to a Modern Dilemma

The energy of the sun has been used for heat and power for thousands of years. Many different devices, designs, and ideas have been used down through the ages, some successfully, others with less impressive results. A list of all of the ideas for using the energy of the sun would be overwhelming, and would include devices such as solar motors and solar water heaters, solar architecture and landscaping and solar electricity generation.

There are two ways to describe the use of solar energy. The sun's energy can be used in either "active" or "passive" systems. An "active" system is one in which some sort of mechanical activity is used to generate energy. A wind turbine is a good example of an active system; it uses some form of mechanical device to deliver energy in a usable form. Solar electric systems also are active systems, since they "actively" produce electricity, although they use no moving parts.

Other means of using solar energy are "passive", meaning that there are no moving parts needed in the system. Many architectural uses of solar energy are "passive" systems. The

A SOLAR POWERED ENGINE CIRCA 1900

use of trees to shade a home on hot summer days, or a house built with southern exposure to the sun to get the most solar heat during the winter are examples. Active and passive solar systems can be combined in "hybrid" solar systems. Few people realize the range of means available to use the sun's energy in their home or business. Before photovoltaics are discussed in detail, we will familiarize the reader with the active and passive solar energy systems that currently are available, to provide a basis of understanding for the following chapters.

Passive Solar Systems

In our rush to identify energy alternatives, our technological prowess often leads us to consider only complex technological means to satisfy our thirst for energy. But passive solar systems or "soft technologies," i.e., the use of natural methods to utilize the power of the sun, also can make a significant contribution.

The most widely accepted definition of a passive solar heating and cooling system describes it as one in which heat energy flows--from collection to storage to distribution--by natural means through a building. The system can function quite well without any other source of power. Passive solar buildings are designed to take advantage of their environments in order to collect and hold heat in winter, and reject heat in summer. Heat can be controlled by insulation, by providing shade and can be varied within the building by opening or closing different spaces to each other.

Passive solar systems do not employ mechanical means to use the sun's energy. Instead, the system is integral to the design of the building; the heating and cooling systems must be designed as an intrinsic part of the structure. Because the

A – DIRECT LOSS – Natural Ventilation
B – DIRECT LOSS – Induced Ventilation
C – DIRECT LOSS – Openable Roof
D – INDIRECT LOSS – Trombe Wall
E – INDIRECT LOSS – Roof Pond
F – INDIRECT LOSS – Earth Integration
G – ISOLATED LOSS – Coolth Field

SOME OF THE MANY FORMS OF PASSIVE SOLAR COOLING

passive system relies on design, its operation is dependent upon the construction and organization of the building, not upon external equipment which is installed.

Passive solar systems are well understood, and have the potential for wide use. For many years, with traditional energy costs very low, architecture designed to take advantage of solar energy was not considered an essential element in the design and construction of our homes and businesses. But with rising energy prices, it has become important to attempt to incorporate passive design into our buildings. Many people believe that the use of solar energy must consider not just active, but also passive systems, in a hybrid configuration if possible. Only by fully utilizing the sun can we maintain our standard of living in the face of continually changing energy prices and supplies.

Wind Energy Systems (WECS)

Although few people associate the wind with the sun, wind energy is actually a form of solar energy. When the sun heats the earth, this heat is dissipated into the surrounding air. As the air close to the ground warms, it tends to rise, leaving a void below. Cooler air rushes into this void, causing what we call wind.

"Wind Energy Conversion Systems" (WECS), or, as they are commonly called, "windmills", have been used for many years to generate useful power. We have all seen pictures of the windmills of Holland with their big, cloth-covered blades, which were used to pump water for irrigation or to mill grains. In the frontier days in the United States, windmills were used

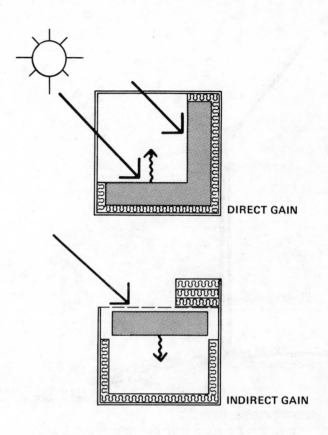

DIRECT GAIN

INDIRECT GAIN

ISOLATED GAIN

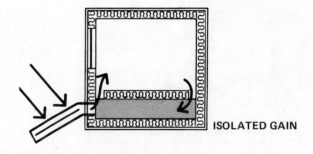

FORMS OF PASSIVE SOLAR HEATING

on farms to bring water up from deep wells. Since these times, use of wind energy has become much more sophisticated, (as has the name), with WECS's scientifically designed to capture the greatest amount of energy from the wind, and convert as much as possible to usable energy.

While the windmills of old were squat with four or more heavy wooded blades, today's WECS's are often mounted on high masts or towers, and have light blades of a variety of shapes and sizes. Some common types are the propeller, Savonius, and Darrieus devices. Each type of WECS has different operating characteristics such as limits on efficiency and varying rotation speeds, and as a result, each type has applications to which it is best suited.

The best locations for wind generators are in open areas such as many parts of the mid and southwestern United States, or in high places such as mountain tops and hillsides. In these regions several photovoltaics/wind turbine combination energy systems are being used. Because there often is wind during the evening and at night when the sun is not shining, the photovoltaics/wind turbine system very effectively provides electricity both during the day and into the night without any energy storage medium.

EXAMPLES OF A PROPELLER (LEFT) AND DARRIEUS (RIGHT) WIND ENERGY SYSTEM

Solar Water Heating

Solar hot water systems have been around for centuries. Originally just cisterns of water left out in the sun, solar hot water systems have reached a much greater level of sophistication, although the basic principles are similar. In the United States, in the first decades of the 20th century, a solar hot water collector called the Day and Night Collector was sold widely in California. Unfortunately, natural gas was discovered in the Los Angeles Basin destroying the solar market in California. But another market was flourishing, this one in Florida. By 1941, over half of the population of this state was using solar heated water. However, competition from other energy sources resulted in the elimination of almost all such systems.

ADVERTISEMENT FOR SOLAR WATER HEATER, CIRCA 1900

The fundamental parts of a solar water heating system are the solar collector, the heat transfer fluid, the heat storage tank, an auxiliary heat source, a heat transfer fluid pump and a control system. The collector may be one of many different types, the chief forms being the flat plate, the evacuated tube, and the concentrating collector.

The flat plate is the collector most often used for home installations. The flat plate collector is usually made of several parts, including an absorber plate housed in a frame box, a transparent cover, and insulation to protect the roof of the house from overheating. The absorber plate is made of aluminum, copper or plastic, and contains tubes with material called the "heat transfer medium" which collects the

MONEGON SOLAR COLLECTORS
FOR PRODUCING HOT WATER

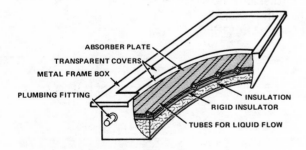

PRINCIPAL ELEMENTS OF A FLAT-PLATE
COLLECTOR

solar energy. Water usually is used as the transfer medium, although oils or water/glycol (antifreeze) solutions are needed in some cases. The heat transfer fluid removes the heat from the point of collection and transfers it to the point of use or to a storage tank.

There are many kinds of residential solar water collectors systems currently on the market, ranging in price from $600 to over $3,000. The least expensive type of collector system comes in the form of a kit with all the necessary components. It can be assembled in an afternoon at a third or quarter of the cost of a store bought collector system. The better made kits use extruded copper or aluminum as an absorber plate. The prudent homeowner, at a modest expenditure, can provide hot water by a solar system and save a great deal in home heating cost.

Solar Energy for Space Heating and Cooling

Solar energy can not only be used to heat water for your home; it also can be used quite effectively to heat your home in the winter and cool it in the summer. The potential contribution of this form of solar energy use is immense; almost two thirds of the energy used in homes and in offices and other commercial establishments is used for either heating or air conditioning. In the United States, this translates into over 13 percent of our total energy use, which is equivalent to about half of the total amount of energy used in the U.S. in 1925!

Most of the parts of a solar space heating system are similar to those of the solar water heating system. As with the hot water system, the space heater will have collectors, a fluid circulation system, a means of transferring solar energy from the collector to the storage or use area, controls, and a means of delivering heated air within the building. The greatest difference is the seasonality of the requirements.

While hot water is used in relatively constant quantities throughout the year, heating is used almost totally during winter months. This means that a solar heating system usually will have to be tied into a hot water or cooling system to use it economically year round.

Solar space cooling uses heat to produce cold. While at first this proposition seems incomprehensible, it is in fact simple to understand. This is a consequence of the second law of thermodynamics, which, simply put, says that heat of itself always flows from hot objects to colder objects. This means that in order to cool a space that already is slightly colder than its surroundings, work (or heat) must be added.

The general approach to air conditioning is to pressurize a gas or liquid, causing an increase in the temperature of the medium. This temperature is then above the temperature in the atmosphere outside, allowing the heat to be expelled. The gas or liquid is then depressurized by expansion, causing a decrease in its temperature. Since the gas or liquid now is cooler than the area or room to be cooled, heat flows from the room to the medium causing the room to be cooled. The cycle is repeated until the room has been cooled to the desired temperature. We are all familiar with the air conditioning that uses electricity; it can also use solar energy.

Most solar heating and cooling systems employ some sort of storage tank to hold heat for later use. Since heating and cooling requirements are much greater than hot water requirements, and since the collector area needed for space heating is much

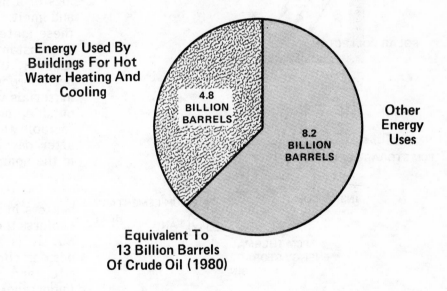

Energy Used By Buildings For Hot Water Heating And Cooling

4.8 BILLION BARRELS

8.2 BILLION BARRELS

Other Energy Uses

Equivalent To 13 Billion Barrels Of Crude Oil (1980)

BUILDINGS USE 37% OF TOTAL ENERGY USED IN U.S.

greater than for equal amounts of water heating, much effort has been directed toward developing better thermal storage materials. In some cases, water, concrete, or pebble beds have been used to store thermal energy. But these materials are bulky and not very efficient, and often require major structural modifications.

One type of storage medium, "phase change materials," consists of a variety of nontoxic salts mixed with water which have melting temperatures around room temperature. During the day these materials, placed in sealed containers in the floor, walls or ceilings of a home or office, will absorb heat from the sun and melt. During the night when temperatures drop, these materials will give off heat, keeping the room at a constant comfortable temperature. During the summer, different types of venting arrangements can be incorporated in the walls, so that the phase change materials vent the heat gathered during the day to the outside, again keeping the home at a constant comfortable temperature. This cycle can be repeated day after day for many years, and has many practical uses in the home, office, or industry.

The best climate for the use of solar space heaters in one which is cold but sunny. For space solar coolers, the best location is one which is hot and sunny. But it is important to remember that other factors besides climate, such as tax credits, energy costs at the site, and other site-specific factors are of similar importance. Also, a solar energy system is rarely designed to provide just space heating or cooling, since a combination of water heating, space heating and/or cooling tends to be more economical.

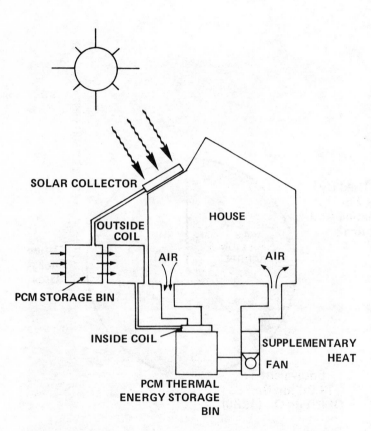

PHASE CHANGE MATERIALS CAN BE USED FOR HOME HEAT STORAGE

Photovoltaics

In the United States today, about 10 percent of the energy consumed by the ultimate user is used in the form of electricity. However, because of inefficiencies almost 30 percent of total U.S. energy use is devoted to the generation of electricity. The only form of solar energy conversion which directly converts solar energy to electricity is "photovoltaics", the subject of this book. Photovoltaic power systems are classified as active solar power systems because, while not using any moving parts, they do "actively" produce electricity.

Photovoltaics is the only direct electricity conversion solar technology. Since we will be using more and more electricity in the coming years at higher and higher prices it is important to find inexpensive and nonpolluting energy resources. Because photovoltaic systems very soon will be economical for almost all homes in terms of the cost of energy saved, and since the use of photovoltaics is pollution-free, because photovoltaic systems, once installed, have virtually no operating or maintenance expenses, and have no inherent limit to their lifetime, many scientists, environmentalists, business leaders and energy specialists believe that photovoltaics holds great promise for meeting a large share of our electrical energy needs in the near future.

To put the use of photovoltaics into perspective, the following comparison can be made. In 1977, the total electrical energy generated in the United States amounted to 2,124,000,000,000 kilowatt hours (1,000,000 kilowatt-hours is enough electricity to power your refrigerator for 55 years). This same amount of energy could be generated if about 12 thousand square kilometers of land were covered

(COURTESY SOLAR DESIGN ASSOCIATES)

A PHOTOVOLTAIC POWERED RESIDENCE

by photovoltaic panels with current conversion efficiencies of 10 percent (an efficiency which could conceivably nearly double from technology improvements over the next few years!). This area is somewhat less than a tenth of a percent of the area covered by the 48 contiguous United States, or about the area which is presently covered by buildings. It also is about a quarter of the land which would be needed if this electricity were supplied entirely by coal fired power plants.

We could use photovoltaic systems to generate electricity in the future, or we could continue to use more and more expensive imported oil, natural gas, or coal to produce the electricity we need for our homes. Already, the cost of electricity to heat homes is astronomical. It can only get worse if non-renewable fuels continue to be used as the principle source of energy. We believe photovoltaics is a more reasonable choice for a secure energy future. In the following chapters of this book we will describe current uses of photovoltaics and, for the technically minded, illustrate how these systems operate.

Enjoy reading. You have embarked upon a journey that may have lasting effects on the way you think and live. Maybe in 10 years you will be walking down a city street on a bright spring day. . . . .

CHAPTER 2

Applications Of Photovoltaics

Introduction

Many people consider photovoltaics to be one of those "exotic" energy technologies that may be useful for producing energy around the year 2000. According to this philosophy, a rather hard and fast line is drawn concerning the usefulness of photovoltaics—these people believe that either it is economical or it is not, and they believe that at present, photovoltaics is not economical. In fact, this position could not be further from reality. Photovoltaics in certain uses has been the most economical source of energy for many years.

The cost-effectiveness of photovoltaics depends a great deal on how and where it is used. Currently, photovoltaics is being used in situations in which power from an electric utility is not available. Another important present-day use includes pilot and demonstration programs which are intended to provide experience with the operation of photovoltaics for designing future applications.

In 1980, it is estimated that close to $50 million in sales were generated by the photovoltaics industry. This sales volume is expected to double annually as the cost of photovoltaics drops dramatically, and as wider use increases demand.

In this chapter, some of the most prevalent and interesting applications of photovoltaics will be explored. The wide applicability of present-day photovoltaic systems and illustrations of current demonstration projects that will lead to major applications in the future will be described.

SUNRISE OVER A PV ARRAY

Photovoltaics in Space

Ever since the orbiting satellite Vanguard I, was launched in March 1958, photovoltaics has been the energy source of choice for space applications. Vanguard I used solar cells to power its radio transmitter. The solar electric system on this first satellite provided power for nearly six years.

The space program that continued after Vanguard I not only used photovoltaic power systems but fostered an industry for producing the spacecraft solar cells and arrays. Prices for space photovoltaic panels initially ranged as high as $500 per peak watt. Less expensive, more reliable photovoltaic panels still are used in almost every space operation which requires electricity. Some of the pictures you may have seen of the moon were taken by photovoltaic powered cameras. You also may not be aware of the use of photovoltaics to bring you the nightly weather forecast from weather satellites, or long distance "live" TV broadcasts and telephone communications. The largest PV array used in space was in the NASA Skylab, which used a 4 kilowatt system for electricity. Did you realize at the time that the live broadcasts from the astronauts probably used photovoltaics as a power source?

The NASA Space Shuttle, which recently undertook its maiden flight into space, will be powered by immense photovoltaic arrays in future extended flights. Currently under development in a joint effort by several photovoltaics and aerospace companies, the photovoltaic array, called the Power Extension Package (PEP) will be used to provide the shuttle's electricity during the entire mission. NASA plans similar uses of photovoltaics in later operations.

Photovoltaics is virtually indispensible in space operations. Even at the high cost of ten years ago, the use of photovoltaics was justified. At current costs, the use of photovoltaics has become even more

SPACE: THE FIRST FRONTIER FOR PHOTOVOLTAICS

attractive. Photovoltaics has been so successful in these past uses that additional applications in space are under serious investigation (see Chapter 10).

How Are PV Systems Used in Telecommunications?

Telecommunications is a broad and dynamic field involving the transmission of information over long distances. In many cases, successful transmission is dependent upon electrical power at locations between the source of the information and its destination. Electrical power is used at these locations in order to amplify the signal over long distances without loss of quality, and these stations are referred to as "repeater stations." A repeater station is usually just a receiver and a transmitter located at some high point overlooking the area of signal coverage, for example, a large valley. Weak incoming signals are amplified with electricity so everyone in the area can receive clear TV pictures or other long distance transmissions.

In many situations, the best location for a repeater station often is in an isolated area. Because of the terrain, conventional electricity from utility lines is prohibitively expensive. In an increasing number of locations, the use of diesel or gasoline generators has proved uneconomical due to the relatively small amount of electricity required combined with the difficulties of constantly transporting fuel to the repeater station and maintaining the generator in working condition. Photovoltaics is the best source of electrical power supply under such conditions.

A number of countries also are beginning to use photovoltaics to power base stations. These base stations are located in remote villages where they can receive communications via satellite. In many developing countries, where there are numerous

(COURTESY SOLAREX CORPORATION)

PV POWERED MICROWAVE RADIO REPEATER IN THE CANARY ISLANDS

villages located in rural areas and surrounded by rugged terrain, the most cost-effective method for day-to-day communications is the use of a satellite telecommunication system. Several countries in Central and South America presently are building photovoltaic powered base stations and have several such stations in operation. The photovoltaic powered communications networks currently in operation have been so successful that a number of countries are exploring the possibilities of regional or nationwide communication systems powered by photovoltaics. Algeria and Columbia presently are installing such networks to link rural villages with cities. Many other countries will purchase these photovoltaic systems in the next year or two.

(COURTESY SOLAREX CORPORATION)

PV MISSILE MONITORING SYSTEM AT WHITE SANDS MISSILE RANGE

Photovoltaic systems have been used extensively for radio communication in order to provide a "direct line of sight" to maintain radio contact with people in remote areas. Such photovoltaic repeater stations receive radio messages from patrol vehicles, amplify these messages, and rebroadcast them to base stations. These stations currently are being used in such locations as the Mojave desert in California for the California Highway Patrol, and by the Department of Public Works and Highways in New Hampshire. In the base stations, the solar electric power system generally includes a photovoltaic array which can generate several hundred watts of electricity, a voltage regulator, and a battery.

Similar photovoltaic systems have been used for radio and television translators in which the broadcast signal is rebroadcast, or "translated," to a different channel. The problem of translation is very similar to the other telecommunication problems discussed above, since often the ideal locations for translators are in remote or desolate areas. Again, because of the high cost of utility connections and diesel generators, photovoltaic systems often have been used for this purpose as well.

Solar electricity also can be used for radio and television sets. It may be used advantageously in order to supply power during emergency broadcast conditions. Where conventional utility-supplied electricity is not available solar electricity is particularly useful. For instance, a major program is underway in certain developing countries to use photovoltaics for the reception of educational television. The TV sets are designed to operate with very low power requirements. The level of reliability has been very high in these installations. Out of about 20,000 television receivers installed in the Ivory Coast for example, the average rate of breakdown has been less than one unit every two years.

As a final example of photovoltaics use in telecommunications, a U.S. Department of Energy-sponsored 15 kilowatt (peak) system is providing power to an Ohio radio station. WBNO in Bryan, Ohio, is a low-power, daytime AM radio station which was selected for this experimental system. A daytime AM radio station presents a good use for a photovoltaic power system since it is a constant, predictable DC load, matches the sunlight hours and often has a large surrounding area available for the solar array. Although the radio station still maintains a connection to the utility grid, utility power is required only when the weather is persistently cloudy and the charge of the battery storage subsystem is low. More of these

(COURTESY SOLAREX CORPORATION)

PHOTOVOLTAIC POWERED WEATHER STATION

photovoltaic systems are being planned, and it can be anticipated that photovoltaics will be used widely in the future for this type of power requirement.

Solar Energy Fights Corrosion

Corrosion of metal structures often has presented a major problem. In bridges, the steel reinforcing rods of concrete bridge decks tend to corrode and swell, causing the concrete to crack and potholes to form. Similar corrosion problems exist for oil and gas distribution pipelines and drilling structures. In the United States alone, it has been estimated that the cost of corrosion for bridges and other structures amounts to about eight billion dollars per year.

(COURTESY SOLAREX CORPORATION)

PHOTOVOLTAICS ARE USED IN THE GULF OF MEXICO

Metallic corrosion in bridges and pipelines is the direct result of an electric current produced by a reaction between the metal surface and the natural chemicals in the surrounding environment, such as in soil or water. This surrounding environment provides the conditions for producing an electric current: an electrolytic solution and impurities in the metal form an anode and a cathode similar to the positive and negative terminals in a car battery. The result is an electric current which acts like an electric battery. In such a situation, corrosion occurs at that area of the metal which acts as an anode, while no corrosion occurs at the cathode.

The use of photovoltaics has been found to be a very effective means to prevent this kind of metallic corrosion. The objective is to force an electric current from the photovoltaic array to flow through the metal structure in the opposite way from which the current flows which produces the corrosion. The result is that the part of the metal that previously acted as a corroding anode now provides a non-corroding cathode.

An element is still missing in this photovoltaic powered current--there still must be a metal that provides the corroding anode. This piece of metal is added to the system and is allowed to corrode, since it will not be part of the metal structure to be protected. This added metal to be corroded is known as a "sacrificial anode" and is comprised of metals such as silicon steel or platinum which corrode at an extremely slow rate. In general, this method of protecting metal from corrosion is known as "cathodic protection."

There are several ways to provide the electric current for cathodic protection (e.g. commercial utility lines, engine generators). However, the cost factors have been strongly favorable for photovoltaics. For example, a photovoltaic powered cathodic protection system was installed in 1976 under the sponsorship of the U.S. Department of Transportation for a bridge on the George Washington Parkway near Washington, D.C. Cost estimates at that time showed that installing a photovoltaic system was about one-fourth as expensive when compared to conventional commercial power through extended utility lines. Costs of photovoltaic systems have been significantly reduced since 1976, so that today it would be even more cost-effective.

This specific example of a working cathodic protection system brings out an important point:

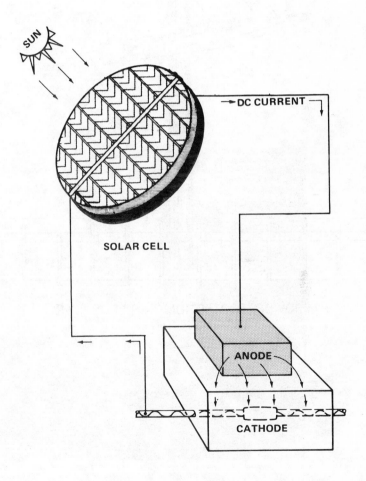

SOLAR CELL PRODUCING ELECTRICITY FOR
CATHODIC PROTECTION

if commercial electricity were to have been used on the bridge, new utility lines would have been extended to the bridge. Even in a heavily populated area just a few miles from a major city, photovoltaics becomes the most cost-effective choice in this "remote" environment. (For the purpose of photovoltaics, "remote" locations are anywhere that a utility line is not immediately available; these can, at times, be in heavily populated areas.)

Photovoltaic arrays also are being used in other locations for cathodic protection. In western Kansas, an oil company uses photovoltaic arrays to provide protection to about 800 natural gas wells. Another oil company in New Mexico is conducting field tests of a 4.5 kW photovoltaic system, composed of seven photovoltaic arrays. Cathodic protection of gas and oil drilling structures will be provided by this larger system. Many other companies which maintain large steel structures, as well as government agencies responsible for the upkeep of bridges, are expected to follow this emerging trend toward photovoltaics.

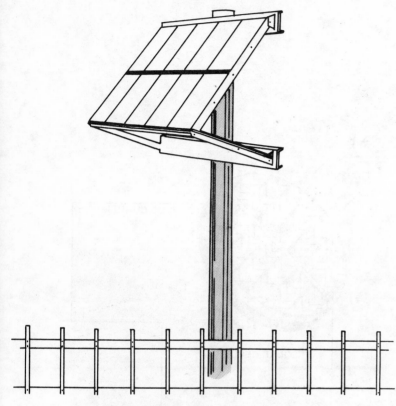

PV PROVIDES PROTECTION ON BRIDGE NEAR WASHINGTON, D.C.

Photovoltaics Applications in Developing Countries

It has been estimated that over one-third of the world's population exists at, or just slightly above, a subsistence level of conventional energy consumption, a level which translates in realistic terms to about two percent of the per capita consumption of western European countries. Such low levels of energy consumption are characteristic of living conditions of persons in abject poverty. Such poverty means severe malnutrition, high mortality rates, and for millions of infants, inhibition of mental and physical development due to insufficient protein in their diets.

The use of renewable energy resources, particularly solar electricity could help to solve the energy deficit faced by many rural villagers in isolated areas of developing countries. Some of the most attractive photovoltaics applications for these impoverished areas will be for water pumping, for refrigerators used for medicine and vaccine storage, and for a variety of other electrical appliances such as washing and sewing machines, lights, dental and medical equipment and household appliances. Of all the solar technologies, photovoltaics may be the most attractive option for decentralized energy used in less developed areas because it requires little maintenance, has no moving parts, a long-life expectancy, can be used in

PHOTOVOLTAICS FOR ELECTRIFICATION IN UPPER VOLTA

virtually any system size and requires little technical knowledge on the part of users or operators. The use of photovoltaics for water pumping can be an extremely important contribution to developing and developed nations.

The use of photovoltaics to pump water has two main purposes--it can provide pure water for household use and crop irrigation. In both cases the use of photovoltaics has a number of attractions; for example, most of these water pumps will use the solar array's DC output directly, with no need for a DC-AC inverter (for an explanation of this equipment, please see Chapter 5). Also, often no battery storage is required because the water can be pumped at the time of day or time of year in which it is to be used. Finally, the installation and maintenance can be performed by semi-skilled local personnel.

The areas of many of the farms in the developing world are in the range of one to three hectares (2.5 to 7.5 acres). In many situations the water table is within ten meters of the ground surface. Relatively small-scale photovoltaic pumping systems in the range of several hundred watts to several kilowatts could be used effectively to power water pumps suitable for crop irrigation in such locations.

Realizing these possibilities, the World Bank and the United Nations Development Program (UNDP) have promoted the active development of small-scale photovoltaic pumping systems in developing countries by funding the installation of photovoltaic systems for this purpose in Mali, the Philippines, and Sudan. With ten independent manufacturers supplying photovoltaic modules, the main purposes of this funded project include the independent determination of performance, the assessment of reliability and durability, and an opportunity to gain a more detailed look at optimal system designs.

Another area in which photovoltaics can be used is for the refrigeration of medicines and vaccines. Immunization programs in developing countries have been hampered severely by a number of economic, operational, and technological problems. One of the main problems is the lack of refrigerated storage, since vaccines exposed to the high daytime temperatures typical of many developing countries suffer a permanent loss of potency. Maintaining storage of the proper coolness requires a steady supply of electricity, which is often not available in many parts of the world.

Electricity from photovoltaics provides a solution to this problem of maintaining the so-called "cold chain" of continuous and reliable cold storage facilities. The World Health Organization and the Center for Disease Control (U.S. Department of Health and Human Services) have engaged in cost-shared funding for the development of an effective photovoltaic powered refrigerator/freezer for just such a purpose. It has been estimated that 30,000 such units will be required in the next five years to support present immunization programs for developing countries. Test units are scheduled to be in operation at eight locations worldwide by August, 1981.

An associated use of photovoltaics is in health facilities. Lighting, refrigeration, sterilization and two-way radios are some typical needs for electricity in the health facilities of a developing nation. Photovoltaics in many cases is considered to be the most economical means to meet the basic electrical needs of health centers and refrigerator projects today. Even diesel-generated electricity is not as cost-effective in many of these situations. For example, one planned health facility to be powered by photovoltaics will be located at the Ikutha Health Center in Kenya. The costs of diesel-generated electricity at this location was estimated at about $3.50

THE MONEGON PHOTOVOLTAIC REFRIGERATOR

per kilowatt-hour compared to $2.30 per kilowatt-hour for solar electricity.

An example of the value of the use of photovoltaics in rural village areas is the world's first solar-electric village—Schuchuli on the Papago Indian Reservation in southern Arizona. (Even in highly developed countries such as the United States, photovoltaic systems for small population centers are often less expensive than the alternatives.) The village has 95 residents (15 families) and is located 17 miles from the nearest available electric utility power. The Schuchuli Village Photovoltaic Power System became operational on December 16, 1978. It consists of: a 3.5 kilowatt (peak), 120 volt photovoltaic array, 2,380 ampere-hours of battery storage, controls, a voltage regulator and instrumentation, and an overhead electrical distribution system. This system provides electricity for water pumping, lights in the homes and community buildings, family refrigerators, and a communal washing machine and sewing machine. All these devices are run on DC electricity generated from the array in order to avoid the losses associated with transforming the DC power into AC electricity.

(COURTESY SOLAREX CORPORATION)

PHOTOVOLTAIC SYSTEM AT SCHUCHULI VILLAGE

The photovoltaic array is shown in the lower left in the picture; the battery building and water pump are in the lower right. The overhead power distribution lines also are visible. Funded primarily by the U.S.

Department of Energy, the system design (exclusive of the overhead distribution network) was performed by NASA Lewis Research Center, while the overhead distribution network was designed by the Papago Tribal Utility Authority. The villagers are very pleased with their new access to electricity which has increased substantially their standard of living.

Another example of an operating rural photovoltaic system is located in the village of Tangaye, Upper Volta, which is about 190 kilometers east of Ouagadougou, the capital city. The primary source of food for the village is grain, which is ground into course flour using a large hand operated wooden mortar and pestle; finer flour is obtained by stone grinding the grain by hand.

On March 1, 1979, an 18 kilowatt (peak) photovoltaic array began operation in this village. The photovoltaic system powers a commercial hammer for the grain mill and a water pump for a six cubic meter water tank for pure water. The mill is managed by a cooperative of about 60 village families, each of whom invested about U.S. $2.35. Proceeds from membership fees and milling operations are used for operating expenses. When excess funds are accumulated, profits will be distributed to the cooperative members. The photovoltaic system was funded by the U.S. Agency for International Development (AID), and the cooperative was formed with the assistance of the Government of Upper Volta, Office of Rural Development. For the first time these villagers can anticipate income above the lowest levels of poverty.

A photovoltaic system also is at work for rural electrification on the Navajo Reservation in northern Arizona. A community water system powered by a two kilowatt (peak) array provides water to a 20,000 gallon reservoir in Sweetwater, Arizona.

Other very isolated reservation homes cannot be served by a community system, so 40 of the homes have been provided with small, individual photovoltaic systems. Each home is equipped with one small photovoltaic panel which supplies 22 watts (peak). The electricity is used to power a small DC water pump and a fluorescent lamp. The photovoltaic system includes a battery to store electricity for nighttime use. These photovoltaic systems have been in constant use, and have provided some comforts which were not available previously.

Photovoltaics can be used effectively on a small scale to provide basic needs to rural villages and increase the local people's standard of living. Photovoltaics is in many cases already the most cost-effective way to provide this needed power. As the cost of photovoltaics is reduced further, the potential uses of photovoltaics in underdeveloped areas of the world will grow dramatically.

It is ironic that where such basic human needs could be effectively served by photovoltaics relatively little money is available to spend. In all of the rural village photovoltaics applications today, the financing for the photovoltaic system was provided by a third-party--either an international organization or a government agency. Clearly in the majority of cases the individuals who will be directly using the benefits of the photovoltaic system--namely, the rural villagers, won't have the necessary funds. Hence, the use of photovoltaics in developing areas appears to be limited to the extent that organizations will be able to aid in purchasing the system. However, there are indications that many of the governments of developing nations are beginning to take a look at photovoltaics to satisfy the basic needs of their rural populations and it can be anticipated that these investigations will result in expansion of the use of photovoltaic systems. Based on the results of the photovoltaic systems currently providing electrification to rural areas, many developed

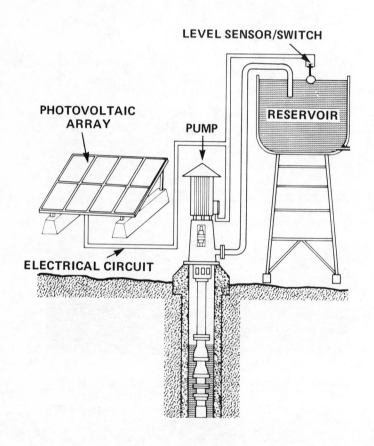

LEVEL SENSOR/SWITCH

PHOTOVOLTAIC ARRAY

PUMP

RESERVOIR

ELECTRICAL CIRCUIT

TYPICAL PHOTOVOLTAIC PUMPING SYSTEM

and developing countries (including the oil producing nations) are exploring the possibilities for photo-voltaics in their local economies.

Photovoltaics and Large Scale Irrigation

As well as being useful for agricultural purposes in developing countries, photovoltaics can be used as the power supply for large irrigation projects. When the area to be irrigated is very large, photo-voltaics can provide power to pump water to crops which are isolated from other sources of electrical power. The world's largest photovoltaic pumping in-stallation is located at Mead Field Laboratory in Nebraska. The photovoltaic array provides 25 kilo-watts of electricity. During the growing season this electricity is used to drive a 15 horsepower pump which irrigates 80 acres of corn. During the off-season the electricity is used to power fans which often are needed to process crops. This system includes a number of sophisticated devices, including a hydraulic control to optimize the angle of the photo-voltaic array. This is a pilot project which is being used to evaluate the range of photovoltaic pumping techniques and related hardware. As an indication of the reliability of the Mead photovoltaic system, over a year-long period since it began operation, there have been only four brief daytime shutdowns of the system. During this same time period, the local utility has had 92 daytime power outages, which is over 20 times more blackouts! This experience has shown that in many circumstances photovoltaic systems may be more reliable and maintenance-free than utility sup-plied power. It also has focused attention on the possible use of photovoltaic systems in areas where the local utility has had frequent shutdowns.

PHOTOVOLTAIC ARRAYS FOR IRRIGATION AT MEAD, NEBRASKA

Military Applications of Photovoltaics

The U.S. Department of Defense (DOD) employs electronic devices on a very large scale which often must be used in remote areas. Such isolated locations include radar stations, field telephones, and weather-sensing devices, to name a few. These installations are often a great distance from the nearest utility grid, and thus require on-site, small-to-medium scale electricity generation. In the past this requirement has been met mostly through the use of diesel or gasoline generators, or primary batteries with a relatively short life. However, the Department of Defense has implemented a program in which photovoltaic systems are to be used in certain situations to meet electricity requirements. These systems can be installed in one place, or the array and controls can be placed on a moveable station. The Department of Defense coordinator for such activity is the U.S. Army Mobility Equipment Research and Development Command (MERADCOM).

The largest DOD photovoltaic installation currently is a 60 kilowatt-peak system at the Mount Laguna Air Force Base in California. The base is located in a relatively remote area. The photovoltaic system became operational in 1979. The photovoltaic system is designed to supplement an existing diesel grid. The Mount Laguna installation represents a major working example of the potential of photovoltaics to supplement or replace large conventional

(COURTESY SOLAREX CORPORATION)

60KW PHOTOVOLTAIC SYSTEM AT MOUNT LAGUNA AIR FORCE BASE

power generation systems. This test system will lead to future photovoltaic systems to power our factories, businesses, and homes.

Another experiment with the use of photovoltaics involves a telephone central van. Photovoltaic arrays mounted on specially designed vehicles are being evaluated at several military installations. A military telephone van with an attached array has been driven over 6,000 miles at different bases in order to evaluate the use of photovoltaics in a field telephone system. This 2.65 kilowatt (peak) system has been tested at Fort Belvoir, Virginia; Ft. Hood, Texas; Patrick Air Force Base, Florida; and White Sands Missile Range, New Mexico.

These photovoltaic systems represent only a small number of the many different systems which could serve the power requirements of today's high technology, mobile defense forces. As the armed forces of the world become more mobile and use additional electronic equipment, we should expect photovoltaic systems to be used around the globe. MERADCOM and other armed force are agencies currently seriously evaluating the use of photovoltaics for a number of large and small applications in the near future.

MERADCOM MOBILE PHOTOVOLTAIC SYSTEMS

Photovoltaics and Homes

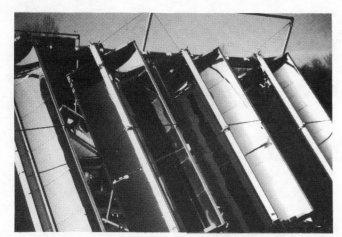

(COURTESY SOLAREX CORPORATION)

ONE TYPE OF CONCENTRATOR PHOTOVOLTAIC ARRAY

The largest potential market for photovoltaics lies in their use to provide electricity to all kinds of buildings. Residential, commercial, and industrial buildings all are potential sites for photovoltaics use. In general, these applications are located within an existing utility grid and hence the cost of photovoltaics will have to be reduced considerably before they can be considered an economically competitive source of electricity. However, given the rising cost of oil and the decline in other non-renewable fossil fuel resources, solar energy is an increasingly promising alternative.

There are many alternative system designs for applications of photovoltaics to buildings. Some of these alternatives include:

- Flat-plate versus concentrator arrays
- Whether the array is integrated into the building materials or attached
- Utility-interactive versus stand-alone systems
- All-electric versus electric and thermal systems

These alternatives are discussed briefly below.

The type of photovoltaic system used can be either a "flat-plate" or "concentrator." Flat-plate arrays will be the best system for use in residential areas while concentrator systems may be a more attractive alternative for larger commercial and industrial requirements. In homes several architectural and engineering options are possible. These options are: the integral mount, where the photovoltaic panel is placed as an integral component of the roofing material and thus substitutes for part of the conventional building materials; the direct mount, in which the solar array is placed directly on top of the roof; the stand-off mount, in which the panel is placed on a support stand above the roof; and a rack-mount, in which the roof is flat and the panel is supported by a rack in order to achieve the optimum tilt angle. For new residences the integral-mount approach is seen as a very attractive alternative.

Another possibility is a utility-interactive photovoltaic system or unconnected system. Where there is an available utility distribution system, the photovoltaic power system typically can be interconnected with utility lines for added reliability and reduced need for battery storage. In addition, such utility-interactive systems will allow the user to sell back to the utility any excess solar electricity generated during the day, and buy electricity from the utility at night when the photovoltaic system is not generating electricity. For uses in isolated buildings or in cases where a decision is made to completely "cut-the-cord", stand-alone applications may be found. Battery-storage is then used to supply electricity at night or during periods of cloud cover and there is no connection to the local utility.

Another option in the use of photovoltaics for buildings is whether only photovoltaic panels or a combined photovoltaic and thermal (PV/T) system is employed. In the former case, the photovoltaic array would power a heat pump in order to provide the space heating and cooling requirements in addition to supplying the other so-called "diversified" electrical requirements of the building (e.g. refrigerator, TV, lights, etc.). The photovoltaic array could also be supplemented by a rooftop "conventional" solar hot water collector which would supply heating and domestic hot water needs. Numerous permutations of these hybrid systems are possible.

The use of photovoltaics in homes will generally not be economical until the mid-1980's at

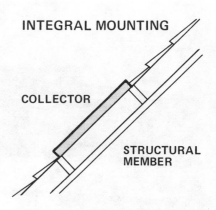

INTEGRAL MOUNTING

COLLECTOR

STRUCTURAL MEMBER

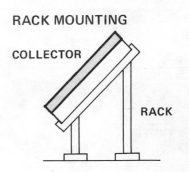

RACK MOUNTING

COLLECTOR

RACK

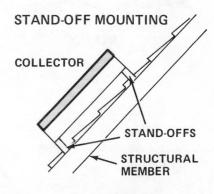

STAND-OFF MOUNTING

COLLECTOR

STAND-OFFS

STRUCTURAL MEMBER

METHODS FOR MOUNTING COLLECTORS

the earliest. However, government and private organizations already have begun building and testing the first photovoltaic-residential prototypes. To develop and evaluate residential photovoltaic systems in various geographical and climatic regions in the United States, the U.S. Department of Energy is sponsoring a Solar Photovoltaics Residential Project with residential experiment stations in the Northeast, Southwest, and Southeast. In the Northeast, the Massachusetts Institute of Technology's Lincoln Laboratories has established a station in Concord, Massachusetts. At this site, five prototype photovoltaic systems are being tested to determine their acceptability for residential use in nearby communities. Other photovoltaic/residential uses that are either on-going or planned for the near future include a residence built in Southwestern U.S. by John Long Properties, Inc., and residences in Hawaii sponsored in part by the Hawaii National Energy Institute.

(COURTESY MIT LINCOLN LABORATORY)

MIT NORTHEAST PV RESIDENTIAL TEST STATION

Many residential applications have been financed by government funds. Private individuals and organizations also are becoming more active in this area. The first lived-in total photovoltaic home was completed recently in Carlisle, Massachusetts. This house has a 7.5 kW (peak) array which is grid-connected. The photovoltaic array, which utilizes square polycrystalline silicon solar cells, (see Chapter 4) is mounted slightly above the south-facing roof of the residence. The combination of photovoltaic supplied electricity used in the home, and excess electricity bought back by the local utility, should result in a net utility bill of nearly $0. In initial tests, the array has exceeded its specifications, testing at up to 7.9 kW output.

Another home which will use photovoltaics to help meet its owner's electricity needs is in the planning stages. This residence will be located just outside of Washington, D.C. in Potomac, Maryland. The energy system, designed by MONEGON, Ltd. will incorporate a variety of renewable energy technologies, including utility-connected photovoltaics, solar water heating and space heating and cooling, heat and coolness storage, and electric storage to take advantage of off-peak utility rates (see Chapter 7). The home should be completed in early 1982.

These homes are just the beginning for the use of photovoltaic systems in private residences. Even today it is a novelty to see homes with solar hot water collectors, and few people have seen a house with electricity supplied by photovoltaics. But the day is coming when solar hot water, photovoltaics, and combination systems will be almost commonplace. That day is approaching fast.

(COURTESY MIT LINCOLN LABORATORY)

PHOTOVOLTAIC ARRAY ON HOUSE IN CARLISLE, MA.

Photovoltaics and Large Buildings

ARTIST'S CONCEPTION OF 60KW PV ARRAY IN HAWAII

There are many commercial and industrial applications for photovoltaics which are being sponsored by the U.S. Department of Energy. Many of these demonstration projects will use concentrator solar arrays (see Chapter 4). These concentrator applications include a 60 kilowatt (peak) system for a hospital in Hawaii, a 225 kilowatt (peak) concentrator system for an airport in Phoenix, Arizona, and a 50 kilowatt (peak) system to be used in an office building in Albuquerque, among others. The largest concentration system built to date is a 320 kilowatt (peak) system in Blythesville, Arkansas. Examples of flat-plate solar panels (see Chapter 4) to be used in commercial and industrial applications include a 150 kilowatt (peak) array for the Oklahoma Science and Art Center, Oklahoma City, a 100 kilowatt (peak) array for Beverly, High School/Patton Vocational School in Beverly, Massachusetts, and a 35 kilowatt (peak) array for a San Bernardino, California commercial building. All these systems already have been designed, and most will be operational by the fall of 1981. All these systems will be connected to the nearby utility which will supplement the electricity generated by the photovoltaic array.

The Beverly High School/Patton Vocational School system incorporates a 100-kilowatt photovoltaic array (which generates direct current power), two inverters for conversion to alternating current, power system control and monitoring, and system protection (from lightning, etc.). The demonstration project has been principally funded by a U.S. DOE grant totaling about $2.7 million. Initial testing has actually shown the system to exceed expectations. It has reportedly attained a peak output of 111 kW of DC power which, after inversion, produced 103 kW of alternating current power to the school system. Any electricity generated but not used by the school will be bought back by the local utility, the Massachusetts Electric Company.

A photovoltaic system also is being installed at the San Bernardino West Side Community Development Corporation (CDC) industrial site. The system employs a 35 kilowatt (peak) photovoltaic array for a light manufacturing facility. It also will be connected to the local utility. The San Bernardino CDC project is funded under a contract between the CDC and the Sandia Laboratories of Albuquerque, New Mexico which has responsibility for the Intermediate Load Center Experiments under the U.S. Department of Energy Photovoltaic Program.

The world's largest operating photovoltaic system is located in Blythville, Arkansas at the Mississippi County Community College (MCCC). This system, of 320 kW (peak), is called a total photovoltaic energy system because it provides not only electricity but also heating for one of the college buildings. The electrical requirements are provided by an array of concentrating collectors. The collectors are "trough" collectors and actually look like a long trough lined with mirrors. The solar energy is reflected from the trough surface onto a line of photovoltaic cells which then convert the energy into electricity for use by the school.

Since this is a concentrating system, the sun's energy is concentrated onto the solar cells, making them very hot. In order for the array to operate efficiently, it must be cooled. To do this, a liquid is passed behind the solar cells to remove the excess heat. The heat collected by the liquid is returned to the school's building to provide space heating. The president of the college, Dr. Harry Smith, has found the system to be a great addition to the school, since it not only reduces the school's annual energy bill, but also provides a practical example of the beneficial uses of photovoltaics.

ARTIST'S DRAWING OF MISSISSIPPI COUNTY COMMUNITY COLLEGE WITH PV ARRAY IN BACKGROUND

Another system scheduled for operation in 1983 is an industrial facility which will manufacture solar cells located in Maryland. The facility will be totally powered by photovoltaic and passive solar systems, and will have no connection to a utility grid. This facility has been termed a prototype "solar breeder" facility, in that the facility will produce solar cells and at the same time be run on the electricity produced from solar cells made by the company. Unlike the nuclear "breeder", a photovoltaic breeder will cause virtually no heat pollution (about a quarter of the energy generated by a nuclear power plant is released into the air and water as heat) and causes no potential safety problems.

Although the "solar breeder" is to be privately financed, the facility, like the government-sponsored projects is not presented as a "cost-effective" use of photovoltaics at this time. However, all of these uses can be considered prototypes for a time in the not-to-distant future when photovoltaics will be cost-competitive in areas now served exclusively by utility-bought electricity. It is projected that photovoltaics will become a widespread "rooftop reality."

Outside of the United States, photovoltaic research, development and demonstration programs have been actively pursued in many countries including Europe, the Middle East, Australia, Mexico, Canada, Japan, USSR, PRC and Yugoslavia. The largest efforts are being conducted in Japan and under the European Economic Communities (EEC) program.

The Japanese Government program, called the Sunshine Project, supports work in all of the major solar cell material technologies. Two areas of great interest in Japan are the silicon ribbon technologies and the amorphous silicon technology (see Chapter 4). In the ribbon technology area, some work is underway as joint ventures with U.S. firms. The Japanese amorphous technology work has shown considerable promise and is being applied extensively in consumer products such as watches and calculators.

The Commission of European Communities (CEC) is conducting its second four-year program. This program consists of CEC funded research in all of the major solar cell technologies including single crystal silicon, polycrystalline, amorphous silicon and thin-film technologies (see Chapter 4).

A major new effort established by the CEC is its pilot plant projects. This effort provides CEC funding for eighteen projects. These pilot projects will cover a wide range of applications, with at least one project in each member country of the EEC. The sizes of the pilot projects range from 30 kW (peak) to 300 kW (peak) with the largest application providing power to a vacation center located on the Island of Pellworm, Germany. It is planned that all of the pilot projects will be operational by mid 1983.

Now that you are familiar with some of the many current uses of photovoltaics, perhaps it is time to explain how and why photovoltaics works. Since photovoltaics is dependent upon the energy of the sun, Chapter 3 is designed to acquaint you with solar energy, its measurement, and its characteristics.

CHAPTER 3

Sunlight And Solar Electricity

Introduction

The issue of energy has become a major concern in the last decade. The public has become especially interested in solar energy. The media has carried stories on solar collectors, the viability of solar energy, solar houses and so forth. But there is still widespread unfamiliarity with the mechanisms involved when solar energy is used. Upon being shown a panel of photovoltaic cells, the first reaction of many people is: "how many of these would it take to heat a house?" For most individuals, solar energy means heat, but a photovoltaic system generates electrical energy directly from sunlight. This chapter will describe the qualities of sunlight and how it is is used as an energy resource.

What is Energy?

Energy, including solar energy, may be used in many ways or converted from one form to another. Heat energy, mechanical energy and electricity are all forms of energy with which we are familiar. In a conventional fuel-burning power plant, three forms of energy are produced at various stages of the process. A fuel such as oil or natural gas is burned to create heat which in turn boils water to make steam; the pressure from the steam forces turbines to turn and the mechanical energy of the turbines drives generators which produce electricity for use in homes, businesses and industry.

Energy is not something you can weigh or smell. Energy is that which is required to do work. Examples of work include raising an office safe to the second floor or accelerating a car from 0 to 60 miles per hour; each requires the use of energy. There are

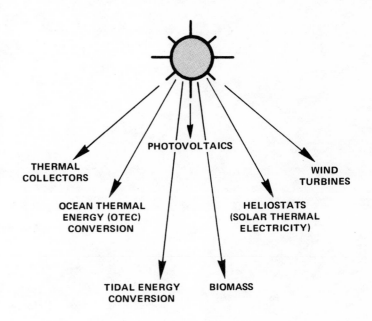

SOME WAYS TO USE SOLAR ENERGY

many different kinds of energy such as mechanical energy, heat, sound, light, electric and magnetic energy.

Because electricity is harder to produce than heat or mechanical energy, it is considered one of the "higher grades" of energy. This also means that in using electricity to run an electric motor or light bulb, for example, some of the electricity is lost usually as heat. The unique property of the photovoltaic solar cell is that it can convert sunlight directly to electricity without the intermediate steps of heat and mechanical energy.

Many people confuse power and energy. Energy is that which is required to do work. Power is the rate at which energy can be used or expended. For example, to raise an office safe to a second floor window requires the same amount of energy whether it is raised quickly or slowly. But in order to raise it quickly, more power is required than if it were raised slowly. The power used in most electrical appliances is described in watts (W) or kilowatts (kW) (1,000W = 1 kW). Energy is defined in terms of watt-hours (Wh) or kilowatt-hours (kWh) (power multiplied by the time the power was used). We are all familiar with the bills for a home's use of electricity which shows the charge for the number of kilowatt-hours consumed over the period of one month.

Where is the Energy in Sunlight?

Sunlight is the medium by which energy is transferred from the enormous atomic fusion reactor we call the sun, through space, to the Earth. Sunlight has been responsible for almost all of the energy ever used on earth. The fossil fuels we use originated from deposits of plant matter, plants which used the energy of the sun for growth. Sunlight is radiation which is a natural form of electro-magnetic energy. Sunlight has many unique qualities, one of which is its capacity to travel unimpeded through the vacuum of space or through transparent media such as glass.

When sunlight passes through a prism or through raindrops, the white light we see directly from the sun is broken up into a multitude of colors. This happens because light is made up of waves with many different wavelengths. Like a wave in the ocean, a wavelength of light is the distance between two successive wave crests. This distance in light is very small, on the order of six ten-millionths of a meter long (.0000006 meters). Each color of the visible spectrum which can be seen in the rainbow has its own characteristic wavelength. Red has the longest, with yellow, green and blue being progressively shorter. Sunlight also contains wavelengths of electro-magnetic radiation which we cannot see but can detect with instruments. These include ultra-violet and infra-red radiation.

Most of the energy in sunlight is associated with the visible portion of the spectrum. This is depicted in the figure shown. Notice also the effects of the atmosphere on the amount of available solar energy in various regions of the spectrum. By a fortunate coincidence of nature, the solar cells which are used to convert solar energy to electricity are most responsive to wavelengths of light which contain the most energy. This match is illustrated for the

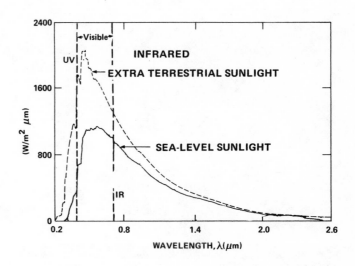

THE DISTRIBUTION OF SOLAR ENERGY ALONG THE RADIATION SPECTRUM

most common photovoltaic cell, the silicon cell. Solar cells composed of other materials have slightly different responses to the solar spectrum.

Sunlight can be described in terms of waves and it also can be described in terms of small bundles of energy or particles called "photons." Each photon is associated with a particular wavelength and has a certain fixed amount of energy; the sum of all the energies of each of the photons is the total energy available from the sunlight. Only a certain number of these photons reach the earth at any particular time. On a sunny day the rate at which they arrive is greater than that on a cloudy day. The rate at which the photon energy arrives from the sun determines the power available from the sunlight.

Solar Power

The amount of solar radiation striking a surface at a particular time and place is called "insolation" (which is different from the "insulation" used to keep buildings cool in the summer and warm in the winter). Insolation includes both the concepts of power and energy as used in the solar energy field. When insolation is described as power it is given as some number of watts per square meter per hour or in the English system as Btu's per square foot per hour ($Btu/ft^2/hr$). As energy, insolation would be watt-hours per square meter or Btu's per square foot. Many factors affect these values, including: the Earths' change of position with respect to the sun, the quality of the atmosphere, clouds, and the obstructions in the nearby environment such as buildings and trees. Only one factor contributes to the availability or nonavailability of solar energy, and that is the sun. Fortunately, the sun is a relatively constant energy generator. There are many other factors which determine how much solar energy is available.

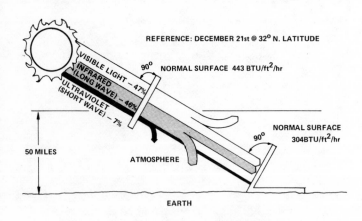

REFERENCE: DECEMBER 21st @ 32° N. LATITUDE

VISIBLE LIGHT – 47%
INFRARED (LONG WAVE) – 46%
ULTRAVIOLET (SHORT WAVE) – 7%

NORMAL SURFACE 443 BTU/ft^2/hr

NORMAL SURFACE 304BTU/ft^2/hr

50 MILES

ATMOSPHERE

EARTH

INSOLATION FALLING ON A UNIT AREA PER HOUR

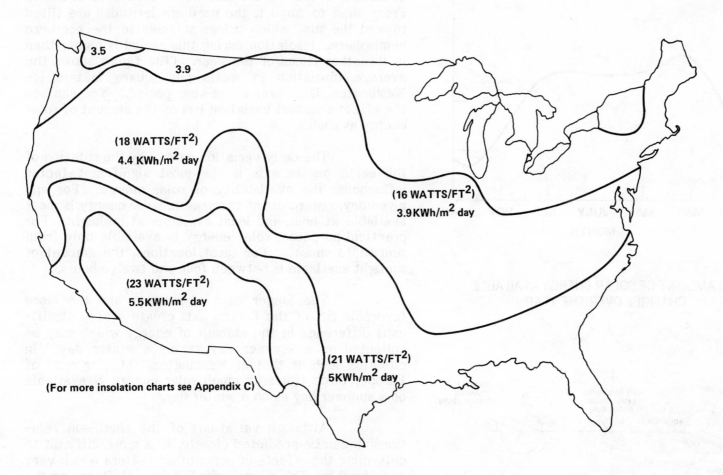

3.5

3.9

(18 WATTS/FT^2)
4.4 KWh/m^2 day

(16 WATTS/FT^2)
3.9 KWh/m^2 day

(23 WATTS/FT^2)
5.5 KWh/m^2 day

(21 WATTS/FT^2)
5 KWh/m^2 day

(For more insolation charts see Appendix C)

AVERAGE ANNUAL ISOLATION IN THE UNITED STATES

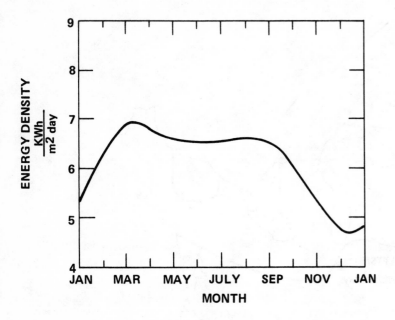

THE AMOUNT OF SOLAR ENERGY AVAILABLE
CHANGES OVER THE YEAR

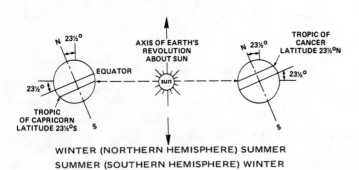

THE TILT OF THE EARTH'S AXIS DETERMINES
INSOLATION LEVELS

The more distant the earth is from the sun, the less energy is available. However, the change in this distance only has a minor influence. A greater influence is the earth's tilt with respect to the sun. From June to August, the northern latitudes are tilted toward the sun, which brings summer to the northern hemisphere. Insolation during this period is higher than in the other times of the year. (The figure shows the average insolation in watts per square meters for Washington, D.C. over a one-year period.) You can see the effect seasonal variation has on the amount of solar energy available.

The daily variation caused by the rotation of the earth on its axis is the most significant factor influencing the availability of solar energy. For any given day, regardless of the season, solar energy is most available at noon and least available at midnight. For practical purposes, solar energy is available only from sunrise to sunset. For most locations, the amount of sunlight available is between four and twelve hours.

The longer days of summer and the more favorable tilt of the Earth's axis create a very significant difference in the amount of energy which may be collected on a summer day versus a winter day. In climates such as that of Washington, D.C., or most of Europe, three times as much solar energy is available on a summer day as on a winter day.

Although variations of the earth-sun relationship can be predicted closely, it is more difficult to determine the effects of some other factors which vary considerably. The most variable factors influencing the amount of solar energy which reaches the earth are climate and other meteorological conditions. For more than a hundred years in some locations of the United States and Europe, several organizations have maintained records of the hourly meteorological conditions. These records include average temperature, humidity, wind speed, percentage of the sky covered by clouds, data on precipitation and so forth. It was not until the last twenty to thirty years, however, that this data collection has been specifically concerned with measuring the availability of solar energy. Furthermore, the number of sites measuring the data have been relatively limited. Insolation data which would tell us the amount of solar energy available for sites without instrumentation is based upon mathematical estimations rather than actual measured data. The best current information is that produced from a combination of measurements and theory using the best data from each.

Increasing the difficulties in estimating the amount of solar energy arriving at the Earths' surface is the problem of estimating the energy arriving at a given surface on the Earth. Most of the data measured for incoming solar energy is measured for a flat surface facing the sky. This is called "horizontal" insolation data. If you want to collect solar energy, however, it is better to tilt your collector.

In the northern hemispheres where the sun is predominantly in the southern sky, it is advantageous to aim the collector in a southerly direction. Further, since the sun is higher in the summer sky than in the winter sky, it helps to tilt the collector to face the noonday sun in spring and fall. In winter and summer there is some small loss of energy collected, but over the whole year tilting the collector at an angle (which is near to the latitude angle of the site) offers the best total energy collection. However, even large deviations to the east or west or in the tilt angle makes only a small difference in the overall annual energy collected.

The diagram on the following page illustrates a range of "collector tilt angles" with respect to

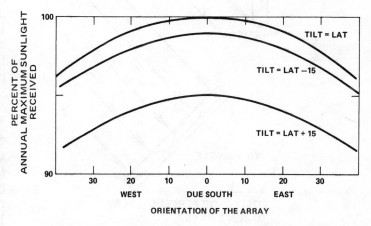

THE TILT ANGLE OF THE SOLAR COLLECTOR CAN AFFECT THE AMOUNT OF SOLAR ENERGY RECEIVED

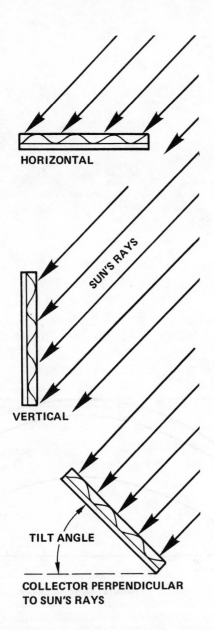

HORIZONTAL

SUN'S RAYS

VERTICAL

TILT ANGLE

COLLECTOR PERPENDICULAR TO SUN'S RAYS

AN ILLUSTRATION OF THE EFFECT OF COLLECTOR TILT ANGLES

the ground and to the incoming sun's rays. The uppermost diagram shows the sun coming in and striking a plate laid flat on the ground. Only four of the five imaginary rays actually reach the collector. Tilting the plate to a vertical position has a similar result. These two situations are typical of spring and fall in the mid latitude regions. In winter, the vertical orientation would capture more of the sun and in summer the horizontal (flat on the ground) collector would collect more solar energy. The final drawing shows the collector tilted to face the sun in this way catching the most sunshine possible.

If the collector were to move automatically to face the sun during the day or during the change of seasons it would be called a "tracking" collector. While a tracking collector will capture more solar energy, it may be too expensive. The additional energy gain may not offset the cost of the tracking mechanisms and equipment.

Most world insolation data currently available has been measured on horizontal surfaces. Recent improvements are an attempt to make additional measurements on tilted surfaces or to reconstruct the horizontal data by mathematical methods in order to provide tilted surface data.*

*Some of the best data available for surfaces of various orientations in the U.S. is that prepared by the National Oceanographic and Atmospheric Administration (NOAA) called the SOLMET (for Solar Meteorological) data. In Europe, the Commission of the European Communities publishes a document called "The Solar Radiation Atlas," and for worldwide data in the U.S., the University of Wisconsin at Madison offers a publication entitled "World Distribution of Solar Energy." For publication list write NOAA, National Climatic Center, Federal Building, Ashville, NC 28801.

For collectors tilted at an angle equal to the latitude and facing to the south, the sun will strike the collector directly at the spring and the fall equinox. This relationship is pictured for spring and fall. The earth is obviously round but with respect to a small solar collector it is flat. The dotted line represents this apparent flat surface and the angle between the collector and the ground (labeled β) is the same as the angle between the plane of the equator and a line drawn from the center of the earth to the collector (this is the latitude labeled ϕ). In winter the north pole tilts away from the sun and in summer it tilts towards it.

For maximum solar energy gain, it is important that the collector face toward the equator. In the northern hemisphere this means facing it toward the south and in southern hemispheres it would be positioned toward the north. At the equator a collector flat on the ground will directly face the sun.

A magnetic compass is one of the easiest ways to locate a southerly direction in the U.S. However, the magnetic north pole and the north pole around which the earth spins are not in precisely the same location. While the true north pole is at the center of the arctic circle, the magnetic pole is located in the vicinity of a large magnetic ore deposit in northern Canada.

The map on the following page is called an "Isogonic Chart" and shows the compass deviation for the continental United States. For locations in Florida, Georgia and Indiana in the U.S., a compass

SUN'S RAYS

COLLECTOR

MARCH 21

β

ϕ

EQUATORIAL PLANE

β Collector tilt angle away from ground

ϕ latitude at the collector location

γ angle away from true South which collector faces

EARTH

TOP VIEW OF COLLECTOR

W

E

γ

S

EXAMPLE OF THE OPTIMUM TILT ANGLE

reading is quite accurate, but in Washington State, for instance, it would indicate a direction 22° to the east of true north or on the other hand, 22° to the west of true south. Thus orienting the collector to the compass reading in Washington State would result in somewhat better performance in the afternoon than in the morning and slightly reduced performance overall.

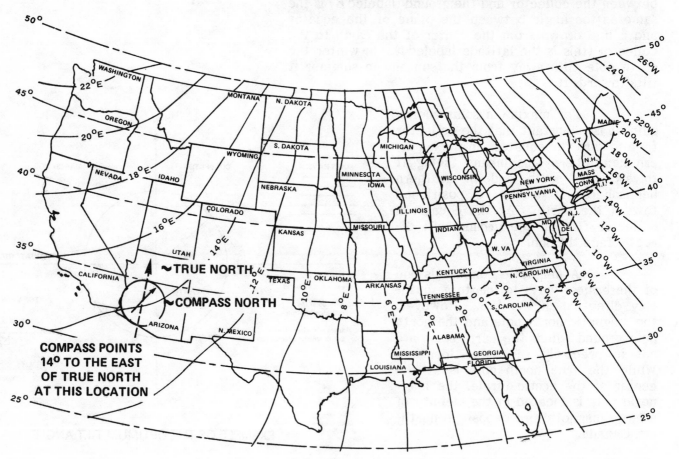

COMPASS POINTS
14° TO THE EAST
OF TRUE NORTH
AT THIS LOCATION

ISOGONIC CHART FOR THE U.S.

The Atmosphere and Solar Energy

We have discussed at some length the effects of the orientation of the earth, the sun and solar collectors with respect to insolation available at the collector. It is equally important to consider the effects of the Earth's atmosphere, including the effects of the air itself, clouds, dust and environmental pollutants. As is obvious on a cloudy day, all of these factors serve to reduce the amount of sunlight reaching the ground.

A principle difficulty for solar energy collecting is that the weather behaves quite unpredictably. In spite of the extraordinary sophistication of the meteorological sciences today, it is still difficult to predict tomorrow's weather with any great accuracy. Predictions of a particular day's weather any more than a week in advance are not very reliable at all.

Because of this unpredictable nature, it is hard to tell just how much insolation our collector will be receiving one year or twenty years from now. How likely is it that we will have four days in a row with only one kilowatt-hour per day of sunshine energy when our needs are to obtain two kilowatt-hours per day from the collectors? Is there a ninety percent chance of receiving less insolation than needed or only a ten percent or even a one percent chance of it happening? Naturally, the lower the chance, the more secure we feel.

The chart shown illustrates another way of representing solar energy data. Included is information about the probability of poor weather conditions. This data is for the region surrounding Washington, D.C., and Sterling, Virginia. The left hand column indicates the insolation in watts per square meter

THRESHOLD*	MARCH							
	.GE. THRESH DAYS				.LT. THRESH DAYS			
W/m^2	2	3	5	7	2	3	5	7
60	85	72	53	39	21	5	0	0
120	68	46	22	11	40	13	1	0
180	48	21	3	1	65	42	18	7
240	25	8	0	0	95	90	82	73
300	0	0	0	0	100	100	100	100

*Threshold assumes that the stated number of W/m^2 are maintainted

PREDICTING WEATHER CONDITIONS

averaged over an entire day. What is the chance that, at forty watts per square meter received, the sun will provide 960 watt-hours (40 x 24 hrs. = 960) of energy for a single day, three or five consecutive days? The numbers in the chart indicate the probability of the insolation being above or below that level for such sequences of days. For the month of June in Washington, D.C., the probability of insolation <u>exceeding</u> 960 watt-hours for three days as measured on a square meter of horizontal surface is only five percent, for five days it drops to only one percent. On the other hand, the probability of insolation being <u>less</u> than 960 watt-hours for three days is 45 percent. This means that there will be a fairly even supply of solar energy in this region despite variations in climate.

Sunlight and Energy

Once sunlight enters the atmosphere it undergoes a variety of changes. Some of the sun's light is reflected off the atmosphere and back into space. Some is absorbed in the atmosphere and comes to us as heat. Still more sunlight is scattered, and gives our atmosphere its blue color. Finally, a portion of the sunlight makes it straight through the atmosphere to the ground. Part of this direct sunlight is reflected back from the ground to strike other objects before being absorbed or returning to space.

The portion of sunlight which reaches the earth on a straight path is called the <u>direct component</u> of solar energy. On a clear day, the direct component comprises most of the energy reaching a solar collector if the collector is pointed toward the sun. On a hazy day, (one which is bright but still overcast) most of the direct component is scattered.

When the sunlight has been scattered, but still reaches the earth from all angles it is referred to as the <u>diffuse component</u> of solar energy. The diffuse

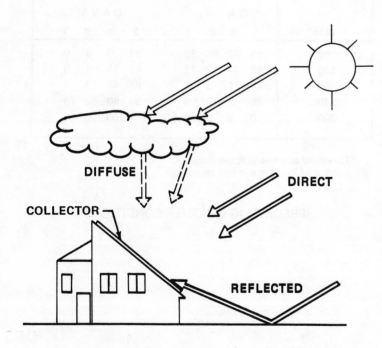

DIFFUSE

DIRECT

COLLECTOR

REFLECTED

THE DIFFERENT COMPONENTS OF SUNLIGHT

component can carry a considerable amount of solar energy, as you know if you have been to the beach on a cloudy day and received a painful sunburn. Solar collectors may collect energy from the diffuse as well as the direct component and therefore need not point directly at the sun at all times to perform well.

Solar collectors also receive insolation from sunlight which does not arrive at their surface from the direct and diffuse rays in the sky. Some of this radiation is reflected from the ground to strike the collector. When the ground in front of the collector is grass or pavement, the amount of insolation reaching the collector by ground reflection is very slight. However, reflected light from bright fresh snow can substantially improve the performance of a collector.

The many factors which have been discussed so far make the estimation of solar energy arriving at any particular collector surface hard to predict. To what extent is the sky diffusing sunlight on any particular day? How much does the ground reflect in a particular area? How much light is absorbed in the clouds? Fortunately, the data we have is sufficient for the design of most solar energy systems. More reliable data, however, may improve the estimates of available solar energy and enable designers to specify smaller systems to meet the same needs and also reduce costs.

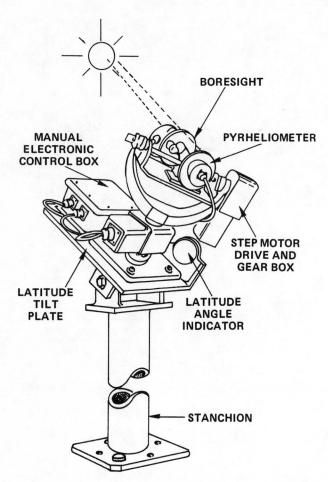

BORESIGHT

PYRHELIOMETER

MANUAL
ELECTRONIC
CONTROL BOX

STEP MOTOR
DRIVE AND
GEAR BOX

LATITUDE
TILT
PLATE

LATITUDE
ANGLE
INDICATOR

STANCHION

A TRACKING PYRHELIOMETER

Measuring Sunlight

One of the major difficulties in obtaining accurate measurements in the past has been variability in the equipment. Data taken on one instrument did not agree with that taken by another. Sometimes even the same instrument will not work with the same accuracy in two different positions. For instance, different accuracy may result in an attempt to measure and compare horizontal solar energy to energy reaching a tilted surface.

The "pyronometer" measures both the direct and diffuse components of sunlight. When a pyronometer is used with a shade ring, which is placed across it to block the direct sunlight as the sun crosses the sky, it measures just the diffuse component. Using two pyronometers it is then possible to measure direct, diffuse and total radiation at a particular location.

The "solar pyrheliometer" is used to measure the direct component of solar energy. The picture shows a pyrheliometer mounted on a device which follows (tracks) the sun's position all day. This tracking mechanism permits continuous daily measurements. By following the sun in this fashion, it is possible to better understand the effects of the atmosphere and the variation of solar energy over time.

What Sites are Best for Collecting Solar Energy?

In addition to knowing the amount of solar radiation for a general location, it also is necessary to know quite a bit about the specific site where one intends to locate a solar energy system. Solar energy system designers might diagram a sun path plan showing the portion of the sky from which the insolation is coming throughout the year. Using surveying equipment or even simple homemade angle finders and a compass, it is possible to sketch a solar "window" for any location if the latitude is known.

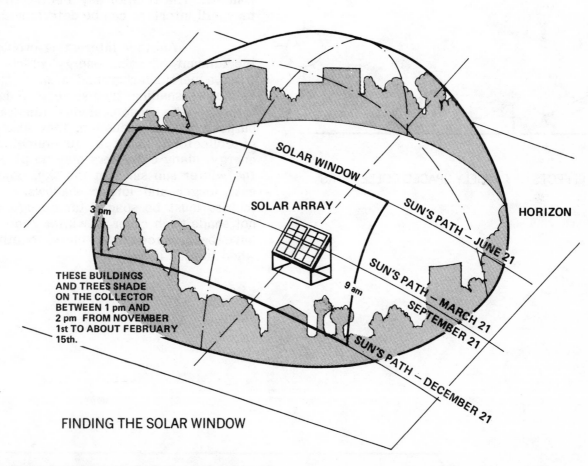

FINDING THE SOLAR WINDOW

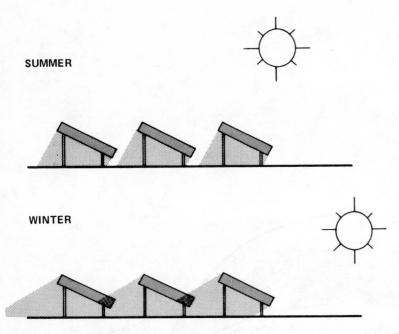

SUMMER

WINTER

THE EFFECTS OF CLOSELY SPACED COLLECTORS

In this particular case the solar window is bounded on the two sides by lines representing 9 a.m. and 3 p.m. These lines show that sunlight arriving between 9 and 3 is the most significant contributor of energy, if other conditions are also adequate.

What if there are tall trees nearby? What buildings or other structures might shade the solar collectors? By measuring the angle from the collector location to the tops of these obstructions, these objects can be plotted on the diagram along with the solar window. The time of day and the time of year at which they will interfere can be determined.

Another interesting problem which restricts the amount of solar energy which may be collected from a particular ground area is the problem of the collectors shading themselves. Solar houses are pictured in the accompanying illustration, but for the purpose of this discussion, they also could be a "field" of collectors. That is, to collect a large amount of energy, many collectors may be placed in an area. As the winter sun sinks in the sky, objects on the ground cast longer and longer shadows. Consequently, collectors must be spaced far enough apart that they do not shade each other in winter even though they might have been placed very close together in the summer when the sun is high.

From Solar Energy to Electricity

So far in this chapter we have discussed the many sources of energy loss which occur between the sun and the solar collector. These include the location of the earth in relation to the sun, the atmosphere, clouds, and shading from trees or buildings. But we have yet to mention the biggest loss of all: the losses due to energy conversion, i.e. the converting of one form of energy into another, chiefly to produce electrical energy.

All energy conversion systems contain inefficiencies. In a conventional electric utility power plant (using steam to run turbines) there are losses between all of the separate energy processes which are required to produce electricity. When fuel is burned to produce steam some heat escapes from the combustion process. When the steam turns the turbines, more heat escapes, and finally when the turbines turn the generators to make electricity some of the mechanical energy turns to heat again and is lost. Just counting the losses from the burning of the fuel to the production of electricity about 70 percent of the full potential energy of the fuel is lost, and only 30 percent is turned into electricity.

A silicon solar cell can send out ten percent of the energy collected as electricity. The rest is lost in the conversion from light to electrical energy within the silicon solar cell.

One major cause of this loss is that the solar cell does not respond equally well to all wavelengths of light. Recalling the figures in the solar spectrum section at the beginning of this chapter, note that the silicon cell is not responsive to light in the wavelengths above 1.1 μm. (.0000011m). About 24 percent of solar energy is contained in those longer

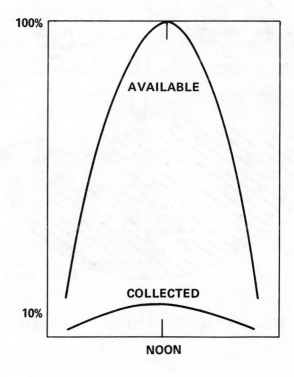

SOLAR ENERGY AVAILABLE VERSUS THAT COLLECTED BY SOLAR CELLS

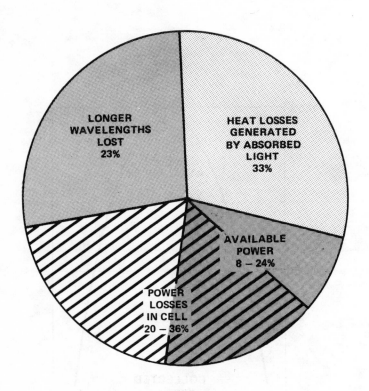

LONGER WAVELENGTHS LOST 23%

HEAT LOSSES GENERATED BY ABSORBED LIGHT 33%

AVAILABLE POWER 8 — 24%

POWER LOSSES IN CELL 20 — 36%

EFFICIENCY LOSSES IN PHOTOVOLTAIC CELLS

wavelengths and consequently cannot be collected by the solar cell.

Another source of loss is the creation of some heat as well as electricity when sunlight strikes the solar cell. In the region around 0.4μm, the relative response for silicon cells is considerably lower than 100 percent. Adding up all the losses due to shorter wavelengths producing heat yields about 33 percent more energy lost.

Finally, even after the light has been converted to electricity within the cell there are further losses due to electrical resistances at different points within the cell. These losses vary with the type of silicon material used and the way it is measured but they can add up to 20 to 36 percent additional losses. The net result is a silicon solar cell which converts sunlight to electricity with an overall efficiency of between eight and about 24 percent. Most commercially available cells have efficiencies around eight to 15 percent, while laboratory cells have been demonstrated with up to 19 percent efficiencies. To date no 24 percent efficient cells have been made though it is the estimated limit theoretically possible. Solar cells made from materials other than silicon will have different practical and theoretical conversion efficiencies from those made with silicon. However, even at these efficiencies, solar cells are quite effective at producing electricity.

The next chapter will provide greater insight into the composition, manufacture and function of solar cells. The nature of energy from the sun and the process by which it is converted to electricity form the foundation for understanding the systems which provide useful solar electricity for a variety of applications. These are described in later chapters.

CHAPTER 4

Solar Electric Generators

Introduction

In Chapter 3, we discussed the various ways to measure the energy in sunlight. But sunlight alone cannot provide electricity. You would look a bit foolish if you set your television out in the yard on a bright summer day and expected it to work when you turned it on. The sunlight must be converted into electricity before you can put it to practical use. To do this, you need a solar cell or "photovoltaic cell," which, when placed in the sun, will generate electricity. In this chapter, we will explain to you how this works.

The Solar Cell

The primary component of any photovoltaic generator is the solar cell. The solar cell is a "photovoltaic" device, meaning that it directly converts sunlight into electricity. This "photovoltaic effect", where electricity is produced when certain materials are illuminated, is a natural phenomenon which was noted as early as the 1830's. However, it took the genius of Albert Einstein, working in the early part of this century, to unravel the complex physical phenomenon behind the photovoltaic effect. He was awarded the 1921 Nobel prize in part for this work. Later developments brought these theoretical concepts to fruition as experiments continued with material having photoelectric (the ability to convert light energy into electrical energy) properties. In the 1950's the first efficient photovoltaic cell was produced by Bell Laboratories, initiating the process that has now led to low-cost commercially available photovoltaic cells.

(COURTESY JET PROPULSION LABORATORY)

SINGLE CRYSTAL SILICON INGOT, WAFERS,
AND CELLS

(COURTESY SOLAREX CORPORATION)

SEMICRYSTALLINE SILICON CAST INGOT,
WAFERS AND CELL

The solar cell is actually a semiconductor. A semiconductor is a device, composed of material, such as silicon, germanium (an element), or lead sulfide, whose ability to conduct electricity lies somewhere between a good conductor (i.e. metal) and a good insulator (i.e. glass). Therefore it is called a semi-(half) conductor. Silicon is one of the most common semiconductor materials, and is by far the most commonly used material in solar cells today. Silicon makes up a fourth of the earth's crust and is the second most abundant element found in nature. It is commonly found as a compound which contains oxygen. For example, quartz and sand are both basically compounds made up of silicon and oxygen.

Before a silicon-containing material can be used in solar cells, it must first be purified into a form which permits the production of high efficiency solar cells. A major source of this material has been the very pure (one impurity part per billion pure) material made by the "Siemens" process. Through the Seimens process, a large electric charge is used to create the very intense heat required to purify the silicon material. Much of this very pure silicon is used by the semiconductor industry to manufacture computer "chips" and other devices. The photovoltaic industry has been using this "semiconductor" grade silicon, but, with the increasing demand for photovoltaics, the industry now is using other means to assure an adequate supply of pure silicon.

Next, the silicon must be prepared so that it can be formed into what are called "wafers," which are the actual solar cells before they have been modified to produce electricity from the sun. The wafers are made by several different processes. The most widely used process until a few years ago, was a method that uses a large single crystal ingot of silicon (about the size of a wooden fence post). This ingot is then cut or sliced into the thin wafers. Currently, other methods are being used or tested for use in making silicon wafers. These include pouring the molten silicon into a mold, letting it harden (a process called "casting"), and then cutting the resulting "brick" or "ingot," into wafers. Another process produces long, thin ribbons of silicon which only have to be cut into segments to produce wafers. Finally a method is being tested in which the silicon is sprayed onto ceramic or glass to make the wafer.

Up until now, only silicon has been discussed as the raw material used for solar cells. While silicon currently is the primary material used in photovoltaic cells, many other materials display a photovoltaic effect. The qualities of these materials for solar cell use is currently being investigated.

Two materials presently under investigation are cadmium sulfide (CdS) and gallium arsenide (GaAs). Although production lines for cadmium sulfide photovoltaic panels presently exist, neither cadmium sulfide nor gallium arsenide have reached the same level of development as silicon. Cadmium sulfide solar cells have been demonstrated with laboratory efficiencies of about six percent, whereas commercial silicon cells have operating efficiencies ranging

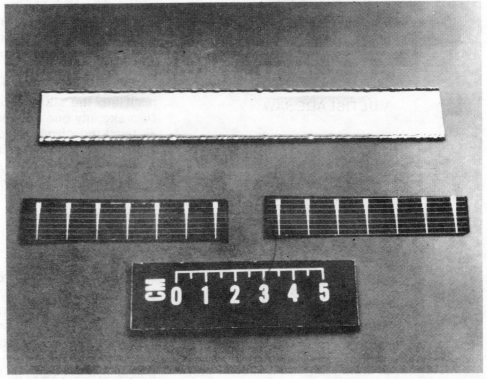

(COURTESY WESTINGHOUSE CORPORATION)

THIN-FILM RIBBON SILICON WAFER AND CELLS

I.D. * SAW

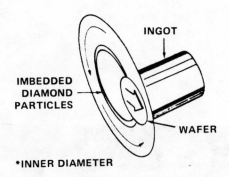

INGOT

IMBEDDED
DIAMOND
PARTICLES

WAFER

*INNER DIAMETER

MULTIBLADE SAW

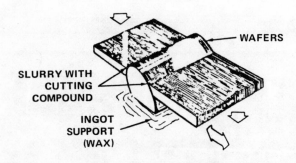

WAFERS

SLURRY WITH
CUTTING
COMPOUND

INGOT
SUPPORT
(WAX)

METHODS FOR SAWING SILICON WAFERS

from 10 to 12 percent. In addition, supplies of cadmium are limited and the hazards associated with its use on homes and businesses are not fully understood. Gallium arsenide, unlike cadmium sulfide, is a very efficient semiconductor which is used successfully in the semiconductor industry. But as a source for photovoltaic materials for widespread use, gallium arsenide probably will not be well-suited because of its high cost and relative toxicity.

While research into all these material and device concepts will continue as a natural means of seeking improvements, silicon is still the primary commercial material being used by the industry today. As a consequence, improvements in photovoltaic efficiency are more likely to be achieved with silicon related developments, at least in the near future.

Returning to the making of solar cells, once purified, the silicon that is cut into wafers can be used to make any one of a number of semiconductor devices--integrated-circuits ("chips"), transistors, or solar cells. When the highly purified silicon is used for photovoltaics, small amounts of other materials must be added to the wafer. However, only certain materials will be appropriate and they must be added (or "doped") in precise amounts. The doped silicon, or other semiconductor material, will then contain a built-in electric field.

One way to understand this phenomenon is to think of electricity as electrons in motion. In its purified crystalline state, each electron in the outer ring of the silicon atom has a definite place. Small amounts of an element called boron are added to the silicon crystal. When the boron is added, voids (or holes) are created in the silicon where electrons were before. As these voids are quickly filled with electrons, holes are created in other parts of the crystal. Silicon treated or "doped" with boron is called p-type or positive type silicon.

The wafer then can be heated in the presence of phosphorous, with the result that this new type of impurity is diffused into the wafer. Whereas the boron-doped silicon created a region rich in holes (the absence of electrons), this new phosphorous-doped region (called n-type or negative-type silicon) contains an abundance of electrons. The region of the solar cell where the p-type silicon meets the n-type silicon is known as the p-n junction and it is this junction which provides the built-in electric field.

When light strikes the front surface of the solar cell, the light will actually pass through the n-type diffused layer and the p-n junction creating a hole-electron pair by forcing an electron out of its place in the crystal structure. Further, the electric field which exists at the junction will prevent the holes and electrons from recombining. The result is that the free electrons will move to the upper part of the solar cell where a metal contact grid conducts the negatively charged electricity. The holes will be more abundant towards the lower electrical contact. The solar cell may now be connected with wires to a device that will be using the electricity, whether it is a hair dryer or an entire house, which is called the "load."

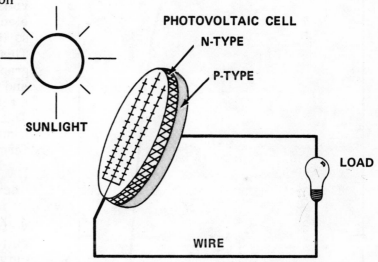

PHOTOVOLTAIC CELL

N-TYPE

P-TYPE

SUNLIGHT

LOAD

WIRE

THE BASICS OF A SOLAR CELL

Solar Electricity = Current X Voltage

Whenever any source of electricity is used, it is desirable to know its current and voltage characteristics. Current and voltage are the two components of any electrical charge. Voltage can be referred to as the amount of electricity, while current, or amperage would be the force or "push" given to the voltage. If a solar cell is connected in a circuit, the current and voltage characteristics can be easily identified. A simple circuit, for example, contains a solar cell, a voltmeter, a milliammeter, and some demand for electricity. The resistance of the load can be adjusted so that it is so great that no current flows through it. This condition is known as an "open circuit." On a graph with the vertical axis representing the current and the horizontal axis showing the voltage, the open circuit condition represents point B on the curve shown. This terminal voltage will vary according to the type of semiconductor material used. For silicon solar cells the terminal voltage will be about 0.57 volts. The current reading at this point equals zero. This point is labeled V_{oc} - the open-circuit voltage.

As the load resistance is slowly lowered, the voltage will experience only a minimal drop while the current increases rather rapidly. At the "knee" of the curve located at point C, the shape of the curve changes dramatically as the load continues to drop. From this point on, the voltage falls off significantly while the current remains relatively constant. As the load resistance approaches zero, the voltage drop also will approach zero until a short-circuit condition is reached. At this point, marked A in the figure, the voltage will be zero and the short-circuit current is labeled I_{sc}. The current-voltage curve, commonly referred to as an I-V curve (I stands for current, V for voltage), is now complete.

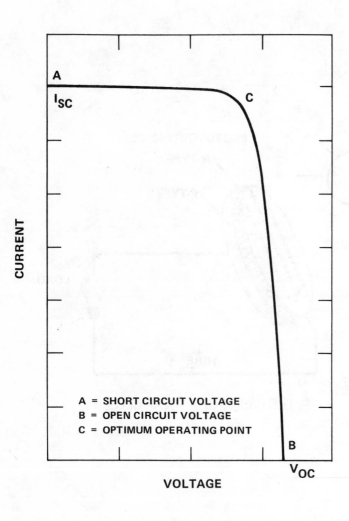

A = SHORT CIRCUIT VOLTAGE
B = OPEN CIRCUIT VOLTAGE
C = OPTIMUM OPERATING POINT

A TYPICAL I-V CURVE

Current and voltage are very important concepts to understand in photovoltaic systems. In any electrical system a certain amount of current and voltage is required. Without proper levels of each, the device or equipment using the electricity might operate improperly or not at all. In particular with photovoltaic systems, voltage and current levels can be varied by altering some of the components or with changes in the amount of solar energy received. Therefore special equipment may be required to monitor and control these factors. However, this is usually a fairly technical undertaking and is best left to those knowledgeable in such areas.

Power and Sunlight

The electrical power generated from the solar cell (or any other generating device) is equal to the voltage times the current. The question naturally arises as to where the maximum power point is located on the I-V curve—or, to phrase the question another way, where on the I-V curve is the greatest amount of power delivered by the solar cells? As shown in the figure, maximum power will be delivered by the cell at the voltage corresponding to the knee of the I-V curve. Peak power and peak efficiency will be obtained from the solar cell if the load resistance can be maintained at values that will in turn maintain an external cell voltage nearly equal to this maximum voltage point. For the typical silicon solar cell, this point will be about 0.45 volts.

The figure also shows the effect of various levels of sunlight on the I-V curve. The maximum value of unconcentrated sunlight reaching the earth's surface is about 1,000 watts (1 kilowatt) per square meter. Notice that as the intensity of the sunlight decreases, the shape of the curve remains basically the same. Further, the terminal voltage varies only

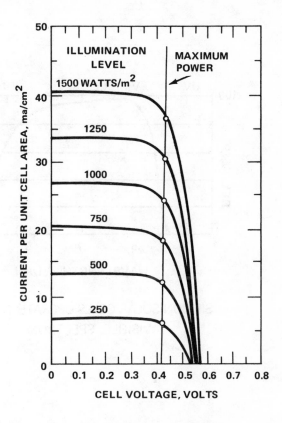

MAXIMUM POWER POINTS OF A
CELL VARY WITH THE
ILLUMINATION LEVELS

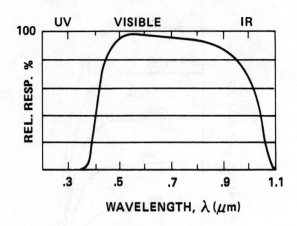

SILICON SOLAR CELLS OPERATE IN THE VISIBLE SPECTRUM

slightly while the level of current changes substantially. Indeed, the current varies linearly with the level of insolation, and the power is proportional to the current.

This family of curves indicates that in all cases, the maximum power is achieved at the knee of the curve, regardless of the sunlight intensity. Furthermore, although the amount of power will vary according to the level of sunlight, the solar cell will generate its maximum power for a particular load resistance regardless of the intensity of the sunlight. Hence, in many applications there is no need to change the load resistance.

The voltage of the cell does not change very much under varying sunlight conditions. In addition, the voltage is for the most part independent of the area of the cell. Just as the current decreased linearly with decreasing sunlight conditions, the current again varies linearly with the area of the cell.

Temperature and Solar Cells

The solar cell only converts part of the solar energy it receives into electrical energy. This "conversion efficiency" for silicon solar cells today generally ranges from about 8 percent to 15 percent. The exact efficiency realized will depend upon a number of other factors. One influence upon solar cell efficiency is the temperature at which it operates. Solar cells perform most efficiently at extremely low temperatures. As the temperature of the solar cell rises, its operating efficiency will deteriorate slightly. The higher the temperature of a solar cell, the less power it will deliver for a given amount of illumination.

The figure shows a typical family of I-V curves for a given solar cell under normal temperature conditions. This is a graphic illustration of the effects of temperature on the voltage, current, and power of the solar cell. The cell current will actually increase with higher temperatures at a rate of about 0.5 milliampere per one degree Celsius increase. The terminal voltage, on the other hand, will decrease at about 2 millivolts per degree Celsius increase. The combined effect of current increase and voltage decrease will be a decrease in the electrical power output of the photovoltaic cell at a rate of about 0.3 percent to 0.5 percent per degree Celsius. This decrease in maximum power is shown in the figures.

The result of this affect is that in hotter regions solar cells will be less efficient while in cold climates they will operate with greater efficiency. Consequently, even though a photovoltaic cell may be placed in the almost ever-present desert sun, its electrical output may be close to that of a cell located in the arctic, even though the latter cell receives less sunlight. This can be a very positive characteristic of photovoltaic systems because in most locations less

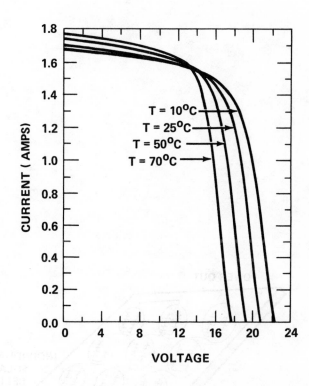

TEMPERATURE CAN AFFECT CELL OPERATING
CHARACTERISTICS

solar energy is available in the wintertime (due to the sun's lower position in the sky) which would otherwise mean less electrical output. However, with an increase in efficiency at lower temperatures the cells may have even greater outputs than during summertime.

Another interesting aspect relating to solar cell efficiency and temperature is that the temperature of the solar cell will generally be higher than the surrounding air temperature. This condition occurs because only a small amount (8 percent to 15 percent) of the solar energy hitting the surface of the photovoltaic cell is converted into electrical energy, while the remainder of the energy remains in the cell vicinity as heat energy. Hence, in certain situations of high solar insolation, the cell temperature may even reach temperatures of $30^{o}C$ ($86^{o}F$) or more above the air temperature.

Solar Panels and Arrays

Up until now, we have discussed a single solar cell and its characteristics. In most applications, however, these cells are connected and mounted together to form a solar panel in order to obtain the desired amount and kind of electricity.

The construction of a photovoltaic panel will depend upon its intended use. In general, the individual cells within the panel are wired together to provide the desired output voltage and current. The connected solar cells might be encapsulated in a highly transparent silicone-rubber compound. These materials resist harsh environments for long periods of time, and are not affected greatly by extreme heat or cold. Such panels may also be covered with a glass, plastic, or a silicone-rubber compound to provide further protection to the cells.

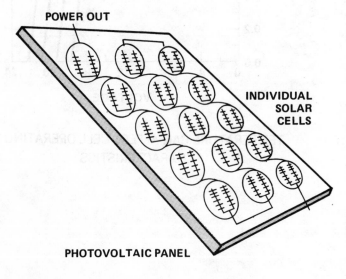

POWER OUT

INDIVIDUAL SOLAR CELLS

PHOTOVOLTAIC PANEL

SOLAR CELLS ARE CONNECTED TO FORM A MODULE

The encapsulated and covered panel is then mounted on or within a backing material, such as fiberglass, metal, glass, plastic, or rigid polyester board. This basic solar panel configuration will provide good protection against environmental conditions. Some extreme environmental conditions such as hailstones, dust, or salt air may require the use of other special materials.

Once a solar panel is specified for a particular application, the panels are assembled to form a photovoltaic array. A mechanically and electrically integrated photovoltaic array usually will include a support structure (including foundation) and other components, as required, to form a free-standing, field-installed unit that produces electrical power. The specified application for which the photovoltaic array is used will determine the number and type of panels that of which it is comprised in addition to the foundation support needed.

It should be noted that the electrical efficiency of the photovoltaic array will always be less than the efficiency of each individual solar cell. This is because there will always be some spacing between solar cells in a panel. This space between the cells will not convert sunlight into electricity.

The shape of the solar cells used in an array will be an important criteria in determining the overall electrical efficiency of a solar panel. Circular cells that are placed side by side will leave a greater inactive area to the solar panel than individual cells that are semicircular in shape. An even more efficient design would use square or rectangular cells. Panels that use square or rectangular cells have much less inactive surface area, and are thus more efficient in the conversion of sunlight into electricity.

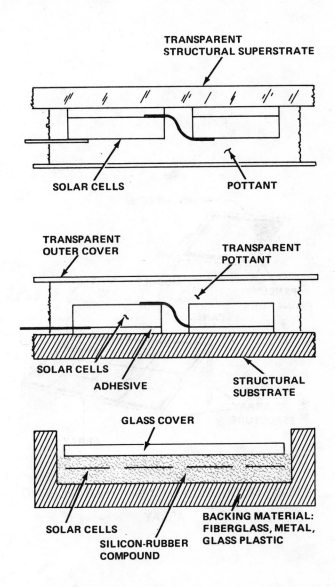

SOME TYPICAL MEANS OF CELL ENCAPSULATION

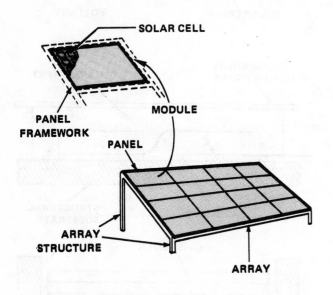

SOLAR CELL

PANEL
FRAMEWORK

MODULE

PANEL

ARRAY
STRUCTURE

ARRAY

MANY MODULES CAN FORM A PHOTOVOLTAIC
ARRAY

Two more aspects relating to efficiency are noteworthy at this point. First, when panels are connected together to form an array, the connection of panels will add somewhat to the inactive surface area, thereby reducing the efficiency further. Second, the efficiency of the solar array will affect how much land area is required to provide a given amount of electrical energy to power a given load. However, the efficiency of the photovoltaic array does not necessarily reflect its cost. In other words, a less efficient array might require more land area in order to provide a given amount of power relative to a more efficient array, but the former array still might be less expensive.

Concentrator Photovoltaic Systems

As an alternative to the type of solar cell and array discussed previously, a system may be used in which sunlight is collected from a larger area than the solar cell and focused, or concentrated, onto the surface of the photovoltaic cell. Solar insolation may be concentrated onto the surface of the cell at up to one thousand times the normal power density of sunlight. Although conventional solar cells are unable to accommodate such intensely focused sunlight, new types of solar cells, called "concentrator cells," are able to efficiently convert such intensified sunlight into electricity.

A variety of concentrator systems have been developed which vary a great deal in sophistication and costs. Concentrator systems either reflect or refract sunlight. Reflecting systems, as the name implies, reflect sunlight onto either a line of concentrator cells or a single point which contains a concentrator cell. Refracting systems, in contrast, will change the direction of sunlight so as to focus insolation downward onto a point or line just as a magnifying glass will focus sunlight onto one point. One type of refracting photovoltaic system uses what is known as a fresnel (pronounced "fra-nel") lens which is a special type of lens used to focus the solar energy onto the photovoltaic cell.

Because concentrator systems generally require direct insolation, these devices usually include tracking structures in an effort to "follow the sun across the sky." Tracking systems also can vary in complexity. One-axis tracking will move the array during the course of a day in either an east-west direction, or a north-south direction. Two-axis track ing systems follow the sun as it moves across the sky as well as following it as it moves higher and lower in the sky as the day progresses.

As mentioned previously, solar cells often may reach a temperature that is well above the air temperature and these high temperatures will have an adverse effect upon electrical conversion efficiency. Concentrator cells are especially susceptible to reach- ing very high temperatures due to the intensified sunlight which they require. Concentrator cells will often be used therefore, in a system where they are cooled by air, water or some other fluid directly behind the collector. When the water or air picks up the excess heat from the concentrator cells, this then may be used to provide thermal energy if needed. For example, a large building application might appropri- ately use such a system because such a building may require both electrical and thermal energy.

The choice of either a flat-plate design or concentrating design is one of the fundamental deci- sions to be made for any particular application. In general, concentrators will be limited to larger-scale uses. Concentrators require greater maintenance servicing and a suitable surface on which to mount the tracking structure. They are also more economically attractive in applications where thermal energy also is required.

Flat-plate collectors have several advantages when compared with concentrator systems. These advantages include simplicity of design, negligible requirements for maintenance, ease of integration with traditional architecture, simplicity and variety of mounting devices, and many years of operating experience proving reliable and effective performance. These benefits will strongly favor the use of flat-plate collectors for residential use, leaving the concentrator system to be considered usually in larger industrial or commercial applications where a large amount of direct sunlight is available on a steady basis, such as in the desert.

The photovoltaic array, flat-plate or concentrator, will generate direct current (DC) electrical power. However, before this electricity may be used to power a load, there often will be several more components needed to complete the photovoltaic system. These components along with their integration to form a fully operational photovoltaic system is the subject of the next chapters.

EXAMPLES OF FLAT PLATE PHOTOVOLTAIC MODULES

CHAPTER 5

A Photovoltaic System

Introduction

By now you should be familiar with the basic concepts of solar electricity. You know that the sun's energy can be converted into electricity using solar cells, and that this electricity can be used for just about anything that needs electricity, from hair dryers to satellites. However, even though solar energy is converted directly into electricity using photovoltaics, it must be properly regulated and controlled in order for it to be useful.

In order to do this, several devices often are added between the photovoltaic array and the "load." (The term "load" refers to the device or building that will be consuming the electricity. If a light bulb is connected directly to the photovoltaic system, then the light bulb is the load; if the photovoltaic system is connected to a house and supplies the electricity for that house, then the house is the load.) Some of these devices include batteries or other storage medium, inverters, regulators, monitors and other "power handling" equipment. This chapter will review these various items, explaining how they fit into a photovoltaic "system" and how they are best used.

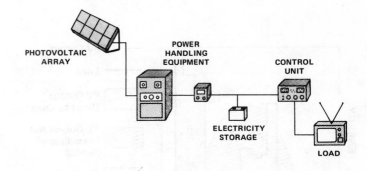

A PHOTOVOLTAIC SYSTEM

How is Solar Energy Stored?

Solar energy storage does not mean that you can leave a jar out in the sun for a while, put a top on it and save the sunlight for later use (although a lot of people would like to be able to do so). Since, however, the sun is not always around when you need it, it is necessary to find some means of storing it's energy for nighttime or cloudy days. Fortunately, there are several means available to store the sun's energy after it has been converted into electricity.

The figure shown presents a sample daily residential load profile. The horizontal axis represents time over the course of an average winter day. The vertical axis represents the amount of energy that is required by the load (e.g. the electricity that is needed by the residents). Notice that over the course of a day different amounts of electricity will be required by the residents. When plotted over the course of a day as shown, a "load profile" is determined. Superimposed on this load profile is the amount of electrical energy which may be generated by a given photovoltaic array for this residence on a "sunny" day.

It is obvious that at times more energy is generated than is required, and at other times, less energy is provided by the solar system than needed. Still at other times there will be a relatively high demand for electricity (in the early morning and early evening) when no electricity is generated by the photovoltaic array.

Energy storage is one method which can be used to eliminate this mismatch between the energy required and that generated by the photovoltaic array. For the load profile example discussed above, an energy storage device could store the electrical energy coming from the photovoltaic array when it exceeds the requirements of the home, and deliver it at a later time.

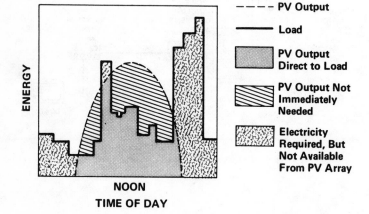

- - - - PV Output

——— Load

▨ PV Output Direct to Load

▨ PV Output Not Immediately Needed

▨ Electricity Required, But Not Available From PV Array

NOON
TIME OF DAY

PV OUTPUT VERSUS ELECTRICITY DEMAND: A LOAD PROFILE

Energy storage also may be used to store solar energy for use during sunless periods. Finally, storage devices used in photovoltaic systems perform another important task: they regulate the system voltage. This last function will be described later in this chapter.

There are various methods currently available for storing excess energy from a photovoltaic system. Some of these storage alternatives include batteries, pumped water, compressed air, thermal hydrogen storage, flywheels and superconducting magnets. Many of the energy storage devices are not considered practical in the near future for most uses, due to either their high initial cost or to their energy storage capability mismatch, i.e. the storage devices are designed to store significantly more energy than is required. Other energy storage systems, particularly the flywheel and the "reduction-oxidation" or "redox" battery (an advanced type of battery) will be more economical in the near future. The best current means of providing energy storage in connection with a photovoltaic system, however, is chemical storage of electrical energy using conventional batteries.

Batteries are common storage devices that convert chemical energy to electrical energy through chemical reactions. Such batteries are called "electrochemical" batteries. Batteries are normally classified as either primary or secondary. Primary batteries cannot be recharged and are used only once. This type of batteries often is used in flashlights, transistor radios, etc. After the active chemicals they contain are used up, they must be discarded. Primary batteries are not used in connection with solar electric generators because of this limited life.

A secondary battery is one that can be recharged many times due to the reversibility of its chemical reaction. Your car battery is an example of a secondary battery. Types of secondary batteries include those made of various combinations of chemicals such as lead-acid, nickel-cadmium, lithium-sulfur, sodium-sulfur and sodium-chlorine. Secondary batteries are used for storage purposes with photovoltaic applications.

Selection of a battery type for a particular solar electric generator involves many considerations with regard to the physical and electrical characteristics of the battery. Energy costs, expressed in dollars per watt-hour, will often be the main factor to be considered. Energy density, expressed in either watt-hours per pound (Wh/lb.) or watt-hours per cubic inch (Wh/in.^{3}) is another important characteristic for determining the proper battery to be used in a photovoltaic system. Other important factors include the voltage and current characteristics of the battery, its intended operating schedule, its storage capacity, its operating temperature range, and its required life. Particularly important is its cycle life, or the number of times it can be charged and discharged before it must be replaced.

The battery used most often in photovoltaic systems is the lead-acid battery, and the best suited lead-acid battery for photovoltaic systems is the lead-calcium type. It provides relatively large currents at a nearly constant voltage for long periods of time. The lead-calcium battery also has a relatively low energy loss, or "self-discharge."

There are some limitations to the use of batteries. First, they have a relatively low tolerance to temperature variations. High temperatures will reduce a battery's life. Care must also be taken to ensure that the batteries do not freeze in very cold weather. The lead-acid battery requires periodic maintenance. Problems also have been encountered due to the release of potentially explosive hydrogen gas from the battery. Through proper planning, however, batteries can be

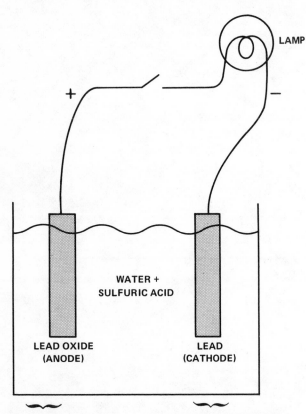

LAMP

+   −

WATER +
SULFURIC ACID

LEAD OXIDE
(ANODE)

LEAD
(CATHODE)

REACTION WITH ELECTRONS   REACTION WITH ELECTRONS

ELECTRONS ARE STRIPPED   ELECTRONS ACCUMULATE
AT ANODE   AT CATHODE

CLOSE SWITCH, ELECTRONS FLOW

A DIAGRAM OF A SIMPLE LEAD-ACID BATTERY

used safely and effectively as a solar energy storage device.

Another type of electrochemical battery used with some photovoltaic systems is one made with nickel-cadmium. These batteries are designed for lightweight portable uses which require long operating lifetimes and little or no maintenance. Although the nickel-cadmium battery will cost more than a lead-calcium battery of equal storage capacity, it is much more tolerant of large temperature variations. Another advantage to the nickel-cadmium battery is that it has a relatively larger density than lead-acid batteries—that is, it can store more energy for a given amount of space or weight than an equivalent lead-acid battery. This battery would be useful in a portable photovoltaic system or one located in harsh climates.

Other electrochemical batteries in the development stage which could be used in photovoltaic systems are the lithium-sulfur, sodium-sulfur, and sodium-chloride batteries. These three batteries presently are not available commercially but all are expected to offer improvements in the future over conventional batteries, particularly since they may operate at high temperatures with superior energy densities.

A more attractive potential energy storage device for photovoltaic systems is the flywheel, the origins of which are almost as old as civilization itself. The ability of a spinning mass (such as a bicycle wheel) to absorb mechanical energy by increasing its rotational speed, and to give up this energy while slowing down has found numerous applications over the ages. Flywheels are not yet commercially available for storage purposes, but recent advances in flywheel

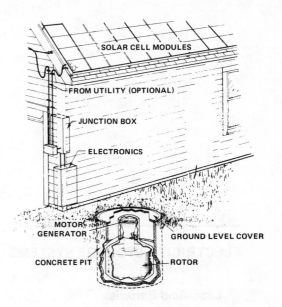

SOLAR CELL MODULES

FROM UTILITY (OPTIONAL)

JUNCTION BOX

ELECTRONICS

MOTOR GENERATOR

GROUND LEVEL COVER

CONCRETE PIT

ROTOR

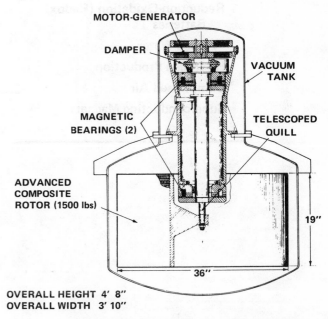

MOTOR-GENERATOR

DAMPER

VACUUM TANK

MAGNETIC BEARINGS (2)

TELESCOPED QUILL

ADVANCED COMPOSITE ROTOR (1500 lbs)

19"

36"

OVERALL HEIGHT 4' 8"
OVERALL WIDTH 3' 10"

A POSSIBLE FLYWHEEL DESIGN

technology indicate that they may have a future use in photovoltaic energy storage, particularly for use in private homes.

Some flywheel systems already have been developed that can be used for energy storage in a home or small business. These devices are more complicated than a simple spinning wheel, but they may be just the thing to keep your lights on when the sun goes down. With continued study, systems may be available in the near future.

Pumped water systems offer a more near-term possibility for energy storage, albeit on a much larger scale. The concept is simple: when excess energy is available, it is used to pump water from one location up to a higher level. When the back-up energy is required the water is released and flows back down to the lower level, operating generating equipment much the same as in a hydroelectric power plant. While these systems are not suitable for storing small amounts of energy, such as in a residential system, they can be very useful to a large utility. For instance, a photovoltaic array could power the water pumps during daylight hours to store energy for use at night. Systems using pumped water already are being used by some utilities to supplement their normal generating systems.

Compressed air and hydrogen production are two more means of storing solar energy. In the first method, electricity is used to pump air into a containment vessel under increasing pressure. When energy is required, the air is released in a controlled fashion to run an electric generator. Unfortunately, these systems are not readily available at this time.

The second method, hydrogen production, makes use of a very fundamental electrochemical reaction: electricity, when properly applied to a body of water, will result in the production of hydrogen (see

ELECTRICITY STORAGE SYSTEMS

Lead-Acid Batteries

Reduction-Oxidation (Redox) Batteries

Pumped Water

Hydrogen Production

Compressed Air

Superconducting Magnets

Chapter 10). Hydrogen in turn can be burned as a fuel to run a generator. The excess electricity from a photovoltaic system, then, could be used to produce hydrogen, which could then be burned at a later time to provide the required amounts of electricity. Such systems, since they use an already understood and developed technology, are available. However, some problems in the use of these systems still must be overcome.

In the final analysis, batteries still appear to be the best bet for storing the electricity produced by a photovoltaic system. In many systems, where a constant supply of electricity is needed, such as remote telecommunications systems, batteries are used in conjunction with a photovoltaic system to provide electricity that is as reliable or more reliable than the electricity we purchase from the local utility.

After this extensive discussion of storage devices for photovoltaic systems, you might have assumed that all photovoltaic systems require storage. Well, you're wrong. Many photovoltaic systems, particularly those not located near utility lines, may require some form of energy storage if they are to fulfill the needed energy requirements. However, in a residential system, for instance, utility lines usually are readily accessible, and it may make more sense to use the utility-supplied electricity as the back-up source, rather than install a separate storage medium. In some cases, individual preference may dictate a total insolation from the utility; however, with such easy access and the possibility of selling excess electricity back to the utility, it could be to your advantage to retain the hookup to the utility. The final decision, of course, is up to the individual consumer, and personal preference as well as costs and other practical considerations will play major roles in the choice between storage or a connection to the utility.

How is Solar Energy Handled?

It is very convenient at the present time to simply plug an appliance into the nearest wall outlet. It is not as simple to produce that electricity and bring it to that outlet. As a matter of fact, this is one reason why utility prices are continually rising: it is becoming more and more complicated for a utility to produce electricity, and the more complex it becomes, the more expensive electricity is to use. Along the same lines, while a photovoltaic array will provide electricity that is as simple to use as plugging an appliance into the wall, getting that electricity to the outlet involves some specialized equipment. Without such equipment the photovoltaic electricity might not be very useful in most homes or businesses. This "power handling" equipment will be described below.

We have discussed so far the photovoltaic array, which generates direct current electricity, and the different means of energy storage which allow energy to be provided even at a time when not enough solar energy is available. However, the electrical output from the photovoltaic array must match the requirements of both the electric needs being served and the batteries (storage). The voltage from the array often times must be regulated in order to prevent overcharging the battery with electricity. Also, most conventional appliances and devices will require alternating current (AC) electricity rather than the DC electricity

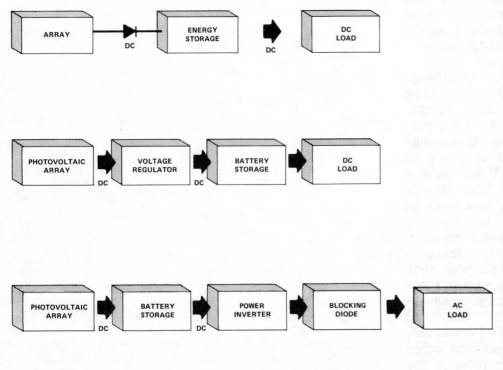

DIFFERENT USES REQUIRE DIFFERENT POWER HANDLING EQUIPMENT

generated from the photovoltaic array or stored in the battery. An alternating current is one in which the electric current reverses direction continuously, usually many times a second. Electrical energy generated by a utility for use in homes or offices is ordinarily an alternating current. To provide an alternative to the utility, the photovoltaic system often will have to include some "power handling" equipment in order to satisfy the characteristics of both the load and the batteries.

The simplest type of photovoltaic power system will be a self-regulated system which incorporates an array, a blocking diode, battery storage and a DC load. A blocking diode is a device which allows electricity to flow out of the array, but prevents electricity from flowing back to the array from the batteries, which could harm the system. There is a direct connection of the array to the battery through the blocking diode. During periods of sunshine, the battery is charged by the photovoltaic array. At times the batteries will simultaneously supply electricity to power the load when there is insufficient sunshine. When the batteries are at a full state of charge, current will cease to flow from the array to the battery and the blocking diode prevents a reverse flow.

There are a number of limitations inherent in this apparently simple system. First, the photovoltaic array will not always perform at its point of maximum power, as discussed in Chapter 4. Second, the storage capacity of the battery often must be extremely large relative to the maximum output of electricity from the photovoltaic array, which will then require a larger and more costly battery. It has been determined that self-regulated solar systems require that the peak output current of the array be less than five percent of the charge capacity of the batteries. This is necessary in situations where electricity always must be available. This requires sufficient backup energy for extended periods of cloudiness, such as a long rainy spell, when there will not be enough power to supply the load or to charge the batteries. Third, there is a greater possibility of the battery generating unwanted and potentially hazardous hydrogen gas.

For these reasons, this rather simple system will be most appropriate for small remote power uses. In these applications where relatively little power is required, it will need little maintenance and may prove to be the most economical choice, even with the limitations discussed above.

What is a Voltage Regulated PV System?

A non-utility connected, or "stand-alone" photovoltaic system is designed so that it will meet the load requirements under reasonably determined "worst-case" conditions. When the array is operating under good to excellent weather conditions, the electricity generated from the array often will exceed the demand. When weather conditions are poor it also should operate, drawing power from storage even when there is an extended period, or "worst-case" of poor weather. In order to prevent battery overcharging and the associated venting of hydrogen gas, under good weather conditions a "voltage regulator" is used to dissipate the excess power.

The voltage regulator protects the battery by "turning off the power" whenever full battery charge is reached. It also is used to prevent voltage surges from damaging appliances in systems with no storage. There are two types of regulators: series-type voltage regulators and parallel-connected shunt regulators. Series-type voltage regulators use a transistor that electrically blocks the array when a battery reaches a full charge voltage and conducts electricity from the array when battery charging is required. Such series-type regulators will consume power at all times. The shunt-type regulator uses a transistor to "shunt" the excess electricity to the ground when the battery is fully charged. If the load or battery can use all of the power from the array, the shunt regulator consumes no power.

Voltage regulation is probably required in most circumstances. A much smaller battery capacity is needed when a voltage regulator is used. A five to twelve percent loss of the electricity generated by the photovoltaic array will occur as it passes through the regulator. However, the advantage of the regulator compensates for this loss.

Converting DC to AC

So far we have considered the photovoltaic system for direct current appliances, but in most cases where conventional electric appliances such as refrigerators or stoves are to be used alternating current (AC) electricity is required. In these cases, an AC-DC inverter can be used which converts DC power into 115 volt (or higher) utility grade AC power. A large AC-DC inverter will cause about a ten percent loss of electricity as the power from the photovoltaic array passes through it. Even though there is a loss of electricity, it is usually easier to convert the photovoltaic energy to AC rather than convert all appliances so that they can operate on DC current. When only a small system is involved, and only a few devices are to be operated from the photovoltaic system, it may be desirable to use the direct current, but this is not a good idea for a large system. In fact, using the DC power directly can cause other problems since DC power cannot be transmitted from one place to

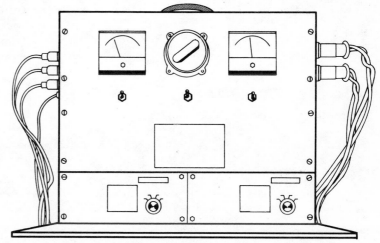

AN EXAMPLE OF A DC-AC INVERTER

another very efficiently (this is the reason why electric utilities switched from DC systems that were used early in this century to the use of AC which can be delivered over long distances with much more efficiency).

Many larger photovoltaic systems include a control and data recording sub-system. This sub-system monitors the electricity from the array to the batteries and to the load. It may be used to override the photovoltaic system in case of failure or emergency, activating an emergency back-up generating unit, such as a diesel generator. While a monitoring system is not necessary for the operation of a home photovoltaic system, it can provide useful and interesting information on the system's operation. Just what the system monitors is up to the user and can range from a simple display of the system's output, to the display and recording of a variety of information such as the amount of sunshine, the operation of individual panels, electricity use by the residence (or other load), electricity sent to storage or sold back to the utility and other useful information. Since each item to be monitored requires additional equipment, a monitoring system will add to the cost of the system and for this reason may not be desired.

Connecting to the Utility Grid

In addition to the electricity requirements for a particular appliance or load being supplied by a photovoltaic system, electricity requirements may be augmented by a connection to utility distribution lines. In this case, the load may draw power from the utility when the electrical output from the photovoltaic array is lower than required. Interconnection with utility lines can be used as an emergency back-up system, to reduce the amount of on-site energy storage in batteries, or replace battery storage altogether. Electricity needed at night or during cloudy weather when the photovoltaic array does not generate enough energy would be supplied by the utility. A utility interconnection would make it possible to sell excess energy generated by the photovoltaics array to the utility. Recent U.S. legislation mandates that utilities buy-back such excess electricity.

The choice as to whether a utility-interaction is included will depend upon a number of economic, regulatory and philosophical criteria. Studies indicate that for most U.S. applications, photovoltaic systems are more cost effective interconnected with the utility grid and without storage.

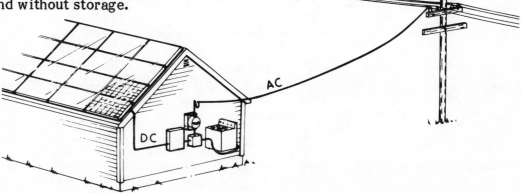

A PHOTOVOLTAIC HOUSE CONNECTED TO THE UTILITY

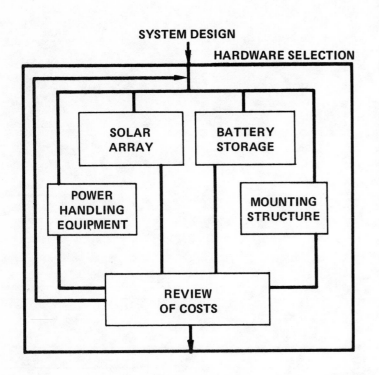

SYSTEM DESIGN

HARDWARE SELECTION

SOLAR ARRAY

BATTERY STORAGE

POWER HANDLING EQUIPMENT

MOUNTING STRUCTURE

REVIEW OF COSTS

HARDWARE SELECTION FOR A PHOTOVOLTAIC SYSTEM

So That's a Photovoltaic System

What does a blocking diode do? Should I use a pumped water storage system for my residential energy system? When I put a photovoltaic system on my roof can I disconnect the utility lines?

You may not be able to answer these questions to the satisfaction of an engineering professor, but by now you should have a pretty good working understanding of just what makes up a photovoltaic system, and as you may have guessed, it is not always simple. Different uses call for different components. While a small system that will be used to charge a battery may need little, if any interface equipment, a full residential system might use an inverter, regulator, blocking diode and storage equipment. But that's getting a bit ahead of things. The next chapter will tell you how all of these devices can be put together in the best manner to create a total photovoltaic energy system.

CHAPTER 6

Putting It All Together-
Or-Is PV For Me?

Introduction

Now that you have a good understanding of what makes up a photovoltaic system, how it operates, and what is required to operate it, you may be ready to ask the question: "Is PV for me?" Of course, some of the decision is going to be based on personal preference. However, should you decide that a photovoltaic system would suit your needs, you may want to do a little analysis to see whether it will be a better system than the alternatives (such as oil, gas, or conventional electricity). If you want a system just for the fun of it, though, you might want to skip these first few pages and go right up to "Designing a System."

A Cost-Effective System

Ever since the energy crisis began, the term "cost-effective" has been appearing more and more frequently. This is a very important term. With the prices of oil and other nonrenewable energy resources continually rising, many previously uneconomical energy resources are becoming economical. If you haven't guessed by now, one of these "newly" effective energy resources is solar electricity. This energy resource is becoming more cost-effective; it now can be used often at a lower cost than other means of supplying electricity. In order to determine if it is "cost-effective" for you, it is necessary to compare photovoltaic systems with alternative sources of electricity.

The fundamental problem in a comparison of the cost of photovoltaic systems with conventional energy systems is the difference in timing for the rate of expenditures. Photovoltaic systems typically will require a large initial investment, but the operating

---

Savings with PV =

| Savings from not Buying Fossil Fueled Energy System over Lifetime | Less | Cost of PV over Lifetime |

PHOTOVOLTAIC SYSTEM

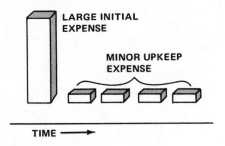

LARGE INITIAL
EXPENSE

MINOR UPKEEP
EXPENSE

TIME ⟶

DIESEL GENERATOR

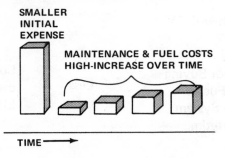

SMALLER
INITIAL
EXPENSE

MAINTENANCE & FUEL COSTS
HIGH-INCREASE OVER TIME

TIME ⟶

AVERAGE ANNUAL COST

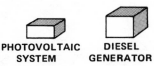

PHOTOVOLTAIC   DIESEL
SYSTEM   GENERATOR

BECAUSE OF THE DIFFERENCE IN EXPENSE TIMING
THE AVERAGE ANNUAL COST OVER THE SYSTEM
LIFETIME MAY BE LOWER FOR A PHOTOVOLTAIC
SYSTEM.

COST OF AN ENERGY SYSTEM IS DEPENDENT
UPON MANY FACTORS

and maintenance costs are negligible when compared to a fuel-consuming engine-generator or the cost of utility-purchased electricity. Conventional engines such as the diesel engine, require a smaller initial expenditure, and the initial investment by the consumer for utility supplied electricity will be minimal, but both require continuing fuel and maintenance expenses over time. Those expenses are growing at a very fast rate.

The basic approach to making economic comparisons between a photovoltaic power system and a conventional power system is to determine the "life-cycle costs" for each alternative. In its simplest form, the life-cycle cost is the amount of money needed today in order to finance the project over its entire lifetime. This evaluation accounts for both the present and future cash requirements on a common basis.

In order to account for future costs on an equal basis with present costs, two considerations must be kept in mind. The first is inflation, which will increase the dollar amount required to purchase a given item over time. If the inflation rate is a constant 10 percent, a maintenance expense for the diesel engine which costs $1.00 today will cost $2.59 ten years from now. The second consideration is the discount rate. Instead of merely retaining that $1.00 in cash over the ten-year period, one could invest it in various ways with the expectation of realizing a certain return on that investment. For instance, an investment of only $0.64 today will yield the same $2.59 ten years from now if the after-tax return on investment is 15 percent per year.

Life-cycle costing includes all the future costs to be incurred and assigns them a "present value." In the example cited above, the present value of the $1.00 maintenance cost to be incurred ten years from now is only 64 cents if one assumes an inflation rate of 10 percent and an interest rate of 15 percent.

A number of factors must be considered in order to perform a life-cycle cost analysis between a photovoltaic power system and an alternative power source. Key factors will be discussed briefly here. The first item is the average daily insolation available to the photovoltaic array over the course of a year. Insolation values are required in order to estimate the overall efficiency of the photovoltaic system. The efficiency of the system is determined by a number of factors including:

- Efficiency losses due to shading of the PV array
- The conversion efficiency of the solar cell
- Efficiency losses due to spacing of cells in a PV array
- Electrical wiring efficiency losses
- Efficiency losses in the battery, voltage regulator, and/or inverter

Insolation values and operating efficiency data need to be determined in order to estimate the cost of an installed photovoltaic system. The installed costs for a photovoltaic system are usually expressed as the dollars cost per peak watt output. A peak watt is a watt generated under the most favorable full sun conditions which is, by convention, assumed to be one kilowatt of solar energy per square meter. In addition, the cost of the other components in the PV system must be considered (e.g. battery and power conditioning costs).

The assumed lifetime of a photovoltaic system is generally taken to be 20 years. Although there is no inherent limit to the lifetime of a photovoltaic array using silicon solar cells, 20 years has been adopted by the government in order to perform life cycle cost evaluations. Costs incurred over this

Cost of Photovoltaic or Fossil Fueled Energy System is Dependent Upon:

- Initial Cost for Purchase and Installation
- Down – Payment Required
- Loan Interest Rate and Duration
- Operating Costs
- Tax Credits
- Property Taxes
- Salvage Valve
- Inflation
- Insurance
- Maintenance Costs
- Lifetime of System
- Depreciation Method (Business Only)
- Depreciation Period (Business Only)
- Rate of Return on Investment
- Income Tax Rate

time period other than the installer's cost will be the annual array and battery operation and maintenance cost (about two percent per year of the first cost). In addition, the batteries may be expected not to last the entire 20 years; the expected replacement costs for batteries should be considered.

There will be many other factors which enter into the cost comparison, such as the cost and expected inflation rate of utility or engine-provided electricity, tax credits, bank financing, and so forth. (Tax credits for photovoltaic systems can dramatically alter the lifetime cost of a photovoltaic system, and will be discussed in Chapter 8.) However, in the final analysis a number of less-tangible factors may influence the decision to install the photovoltaic system. One of these less tangible, yet no less real, influences would be the inherent value of having a power system which relies on the sun as an energy resource and which has an environmentally benign impact. In general, the cost-competitiveness of a photovoltaic system will depend on the application, as discussed in Chapters 2 and 10.

The formulas used to determine life-cycle costs can be found in most accounting books (they are omitted here because they cannot be fairly treated in such a short space). By using these formulas and plugging in the proper values, you can determine how much it may cost to buy electricity from the utility for the next 20 years, to use a diesel engine, or to purchase and use a photovoltaic system. In many cases a photovoltaic system would be more cost effective than a diesel generator or utility-supplied electricity. However, this will not be the case for every possible use, and it is important to remember that future fossil fuel price increases will significantly alter the comparison. It also should be noted that while electric utilities provide energy to the consumer at low prices, non-renewable energy resources have received well over

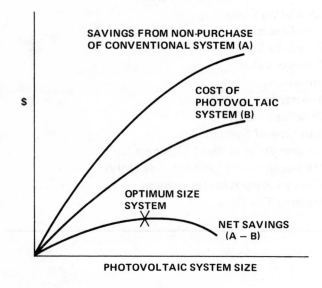

SAVINGS FROM NON-PURCHASE OF CONVENTIONAL SYSTEM (A)

COST OF PHOTOVOLTAIC SYSTEM (B)

$

OPTIMUM SIZE SYSTEM

NET SAVINGS (A – B)

PHOTOVOLTAIC SYSTEM SIZE

THERE IS AN OPTIMUM SIZE PV SYSTEM FOR EVERY APPLICATION

$200 billion in government support, while photovoltaics have received comparatively little. This subsidy is a cost which is felt at tax time, not when the electric bill is paid.

Designing a System

Now that you have decided that a photovoltaic system maybe useful to you, the next step is to determine how to assemble a system. There are two ways this can be done: the wrong way and the right way. While you may get lucky and put together a good system by using the wrong way, we will explain the right way to design a system. Since the previous chapters have described the parts of a photovoltaic system, the rest of this chapter will discuss how to determine which system is right for a specific use, and how that system can be designed and assembled. While this can be a complicated process (just as wiring a house for electricity is a complicated process) this discussion is intended to familiarize the reader with photovoltaic system design concepts. Depending on the size of a particular system, you may want to look at a more detailed design guide before beginning installation.*

In order to successfully determine the system design for your purposes, weather and insolation data are a major requirement because the size of the photovoltaic system will be determined not only by the amount of electricity required by the load, but also by the amount of sunshine that is available to power the system. Since different areas will have different

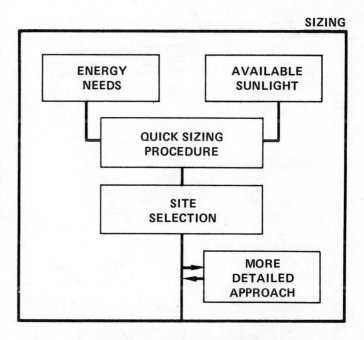

SIMPLIFIED DESIGN PROCEDURE

---

*MONEGON published a detailed design guide entitled "Designing Small Photovoltaic Power Systems." This publication is available as MONEGON Report M111, for $10.00.

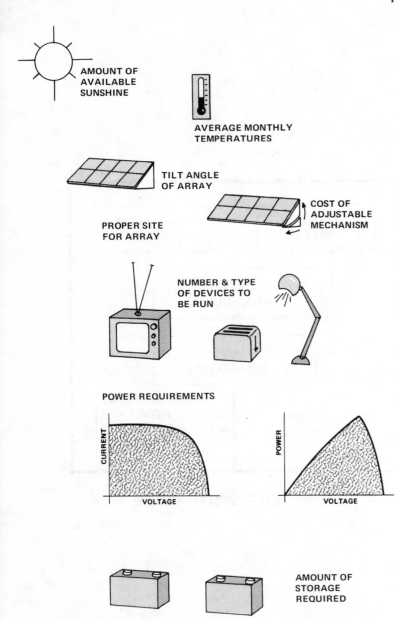

AMOUNT OF AVAILABLE SUNSHINE

AVERAGE MONTHLY TEMPERATURES

TILT ANGLE OF ARRAY

PROPER SITE FOR ARRAY

COST OF ADJUSTABLE MECHANISM

NUMBER & TYPE OF DEVICES TO BE RUN

POWER REQUIREMENTS

CURRENT

VOLTAGE

POWER

VOLTAGE

AMOUNT OF STORAGE REQUIRED

SOME CONSIDERATIONS IN PV SYSTEM DESIGN

amounts of sunlight available, it is important to determine the "solar situation" in the area in which the photovoltaic system will be operating. Available insolation for photovoltaics often is expressed in sun hours per day ($kWh/day/m^2$). This average sun hour per day number will change according to the time of year and location.

Tables are readily available which will provide monthly averages for daily insolation (see Appendix C). Most photovoltaic systems are designed to provide the necessary electricity even under the worst seasonal conditions. In the northern hemisphere, this "worst case" time period would be in mid-December, whereas in the southern hemisphere, it would be in mid-June.

Solar insolation data must account for the planned tilt angle of the photovoltaic array. If the array is set on an angle equal to the latitude of the site and the panels are not adjustable, it will achieve good overall annual performance. However, an array that can be adjusted to different tilt angles during the year will operate even more effectively. Better performance is possible in the northern hemisphere if the angle is lowered during the summer months and raised during the winter. Whether or not the array tilt angle is seasonally adjusted must be accounted for in any system design.

Before deciding on an adjustable system, you must be sure that (a) the system is accessible, (b) it is on a surface that will not prohibit tilting (such as a roof that is already at a steep angle), and (c) the extra hardware needed will not cost more than the cost savings from the extra solar energy gained.

It also is important to know the average monthly temperatures at which the photovoltaic array will operate. The higher the temperature of the surrounding air, the lower the electrical efficiency of the array. Consequently, in hot climates a photovoltaic system will not operate as efficiently as in cold climates. This is why some systems have higher output levels in the winter even though there may be less solar energy available.

The next item to consider is the kind and number of devices to be operated by the photovoltaic system and their electrical requirements. Will the array be used for an all-electric house, or only for the heating and cooling needs? The electricity needed can vary according to the time of day, the month, and the year. Once these requirements are specified over time, a load profile emerges which can be used to determine how much electricity the photovoltaic array must generate. In order to plan for solar electric applications, this load requirement must be specified in power (watts), current (amps), voltage, and finally for the time period during which electricity will be used. For example, a small battery charger which runs on DC electricity might require 7.0 amps at 12 volts for three hours every day.

Both the voltage and current requirements must be determined because this will have implications for the design of the photovoltaic array. Solar panels can be connected to provide the desired electrical output in both current (A) and volts (V). As shown in the figure, when several panels are connected in series, the total voltage from the photovoltaic array will be the sum of the voltage from the individual panels, while the output current (amps) from the array will be the same as that from a single photovoltaic panel.

When the photovoltaic panels are connected in parallel, the total current will be the sum of the currents from the individual panels. The total voltage from the assembly will be equal to the voltage

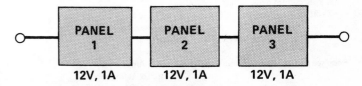

TOTAL VOLTAGE = 12V x 3 = 36V
TOTAL CURRENT = 1 Amp

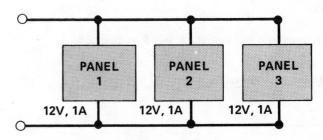

TOTAL VOLTAGE = 12 Volts
TOTAL CURRENT = 3 Amps

SERIES VERSUS PARALLEL CONNECTION

from a single panel. Photovoltaic panels can be arranged in various series-parallel circuits in order to provide current and voltages required by the device(s) which are to be operated by the photovoltaic array.

A simple example may be used to illustrate the concepts of system design. Consider a small rest station located at a scenic overlook in a remote location of a national park. The station requires electricity in order to power communications equipment and a small electric heater. A photovoltaic system probably is the most economical way to meet these electric requirements. When in operation, the communications equipment will require two amps of current, and will operate three hours per day. The heater, when used in cold months will require seven amps of current, and will be operated about 14 hours per day. Both the communications equipment and the heater will require 12 volts DC electricity.

The total daily electricity requirements for the facility may be found from the following equations and is calculated in the table shown. For each of the devices that require electricity, the average daily load is found by multiplying the required current in amps by the hours in use. This load is given in amp-hours (Ah). The voltage requirements for a given device usually will remain the same when it is in use. In addition, the voltage from the photovoltaic power system will remain relatively constant, and the batteries also will tend to operate at a constant voltage. Hence, the electricity requirements usually are expressed in amp-hours at a specified voltage.

Once the electrical requirements have been determined, the power characteristics of the array can be specified. This is done by dividing the amount of electricity needed by the equivalent number of sun hours per day at the location where the photovoltaic

Sample PV System Design

Electrical Requirements of Remote Facility

	Hours in Use	Amps Drawn	Amp-hours Required
Communications Equipment	3	2	6
Electric Heater	14	7	98
Total daily current demand at 12 volts DC			104

Required PV System Output

Required system output in amperes (A) = 104 Amp- hours
x 20% safety margin
(at 12 volts DC)
= 124.8 Amp-hours/day

124.8 Amp-hours/day/4 sun-hours/day = 31.2 amps at 12 volts DC

Number of Panels

Selecting a panel with an output of 2.5 amps at 14 volts DC

$$\frac{31.2 \text{ A (required system output)}}{2.5 \text{ A (at 14 volts)}} = 12.48 \text{ or } 13 \text{ panels in parallel}$$

SAMPLE PHOTOVOLTAIC SYSTEM DESIGN

system is to be placed. This number then is multiplied by 1.2 in order to establish a safety margin. The result of this formula will be the amount of current at a specified voltage which must be supplied by the photovoltaic system.

You can now determine the number of panels that will be required and how they should be arranged. A manufacturer of photovoltaic panels will specify the electrical output of their photovoltaic panels. It has been found through experience that a photovoltaic panel with a voltage of 14 volts is well-suited for 12 volt applications. For this example it has been assumed that this panel will have an output current of 2.5 amps at 14 volt terminal voltage. Hence, no series connection will be required because the voltage requirements are met by one panel. Dividing the required system output by the output of each panel, the number of panels required can be found. In this case, the number turns out to be 12.48, which is rounded up to 13. Thus, 13 panels will be required. Because the voltage requirement is met by one panel, the photovoltaic array will be comprised of 13 panels arranged in parallel. The panels are arranged in parallel in order to satisfy the current requirements.

Although requirements of the photovoltaic array have been determined, the appropriate battery and power handling has to be designed. Computer simulations have been programmed specifically in order to optimize the photovoltaic system. The Solar Energy Information Data Bank (see Appendix A) can provide some of this material.

But first, some more information must be at hand: the photovoltaic system may be operating in a location where the longest period of time without sunlight is expected to be a week. If it is important never to be without electricity the storage batteries should be capable of operating the load for a week without any electricity generated by the photovoltaic array. In our example of the remote facility, this would be equal to 728 amp-hours at 12 volts. Further, because the load runs on DC electricity, no AC-DC inverter will be required.

The above presents a simplified example of what goes into a photovoltaic system design for a small system. On a larger system, for instance for a home, a much more complex design procedure is required. Since most houses run on AC power, the DC electricity from the array must be converted into AC electricity. In addition, regulators, blocking diodes, meters and other equipment may be required. Because such a system design is so complex it will not be discussed here. Some of the references in Appendix A do provide the required detail; however, the guidance of an experienced photovoltaic system designer may be necessary for a large system.

Before you install your photovoltaic system there is one more area that needs investigation: the law. For most systems, only technical questions will have to be answered such as the proper size of the storage system, the proper tilt angle for the collectors, etc. However, for some systems, the proper placement of the solar collectors may raise legal questions, such as the consequences of a system being shaded by a neighbors tree. The next chapter will discuss these concerns in more detail, explaining the various issues surrounding photovoltaic siting questions.

CHAPTER 7

Solar Law —
What Are My Solar Rights?

Introduction

Energy from the sun is the only readily available, free source of energy of which we know. It cannot be licensed, it cannot be copyrighted, and it cannot be taken away. However, for many, it is a scarce resource: people living in densely populated urban areas may be surrounded by buildings which deprive them of most or all of the available direct sunlight; those living in highrise apartment buildings may have only limited access to the sun; and even individuals living in more rural areas may face shading problems caused by trees or other dense vegetation.

The point is simple: the sun's energy, while abundantly available, is not always easily gained. A person's sunrights need to be protected lest their access to this valuable resource be denied in some way. If you are installing a movable or mobile solar system (such as on a recreational vehicle) questions of solar rights and access to the sun may not be as crucial; the system often can be adjusted to accommodate local constraints.

ACCESS TO THE SUN CAN BE AFFECTED IN MANY WAYS

Placing a photovoltaic array on a residence may present unforeseen problems. For example, Homeowner A lives in a suburban neighborhood of single family, detached housing. Homeowner A decides to put a solar collector on his or her roof, which, he/she notes, receives sunlight for a good part of the day. However, after installing the system, Homeowner A notices that during the early afternoon the system does not perform well. After investigation, he or she realizes that the neighbor's tree is shading the solar system during that time period. Should this situation continue, Homeowner A will lose much of the benefit from the solar system. What can he or she do? The answer to that question will be discussed below.

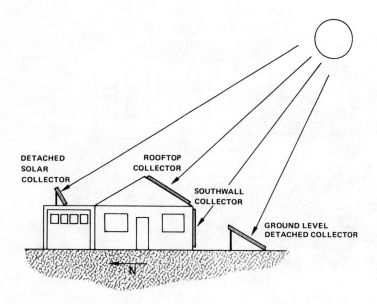

DETACHED SOLAR COLLECTOR

ROOFTOP COLLECTOR

SOUTHWALL COLLECTOR

GROUND LEVEL DETACHED COLLECTOR

N

THERE ARE MANY DIFFERENT LOCATIONS AND METHODS FOR SITING A SOLAR COLLECTOR

What Are Solar Rights?

An individual's access to the sun, as indicated in the example above, is not absolute. Anything from bushes or trees to a new apartment building across the street can interfere with a person's access to the sun. Solar rights have, until recent times, been for the most part, ignored. The conflict becomes one between an individual or group wishing to install a solar system or to have clear access to the sun's rays, and local ordinances, state laws, or Federal regulations. These various determinations of solar rights have several levels of application and enforcement:

Federal: This includes any federal legislation regulating the use of energy resources. From a private user's standpoint, the greatest impact of the Federal government is on the utilities which play a major part in how we obtain and use electricity.

State: Depending on the particular state, involvement at this level can vary from simple regulations of the state power utilities to land use and financial incentives for solar.

Local: On the local level, involvement is usually in the form of local land use policy and building codes that regulate what may be built, where it can be built and how it is to be constructed.

The impact upon a person's "solar rights" resulting from each of these levels will be discussed. However, it is important to remember that, while almost no one opposes solar energy, a lack of adequate public knowledge (and many laws and ordinances which were written for a time when there was no energy problem) can inadvertently hinder the development of solar energy. For example, the historic district commission of a town tried to block installation of solar roof panels due to their visibility from the street and nearby river.

Before looking more closely at these various areas, let's examine just how solar access questions arise.

Locating a Solar Collector

When placing a lamp in a room the only question that needs to be asked (other than aesthetic ones) is "where is the closest electrical outlet?" Similarly, when installing an engine or battery in order to operate a piece of equipment, one need only make sure that it is close enough to the equipment to operate it properly and is protected from weather or accidental damage.

A solar system which produces electrical or thermal energy though, has a unique consideration: it needs light from the sun in order to operate. Moreover, in many systems, even slight reductions in available sunlight will cause loss of energy. Careful consideration must be given to the proper placement of your solar system. Moreover, finding the proper site for a photovoltaic system raises additional questions. One first has to determine where the greatest amount of solar insolation can be collected. Then other questions need to be considered such as building height restrictions and property rights. By considering possible problems when planning a solar system, many problems can be avoided before they arise, thus insuring the fullest benefits from the system.

Beyond the technical considerations, however, equally important questions arise, relating to local, state, and even Federal law. If I put a solar panel up in front of my neighbor's window, he may not like it and may take me to court. This is obviously a situation to be avoided, but one that sometimes can be hard to foresee. It is valuable to know, therefore, when these questions might arise, and how to avoid them. One of the keys to preventing such problems is to select the proper site for installing your solar collector.

Chapter 3 reviewed proper tilt angles and insolation levels for collectors. However, in order to determine if the solar collector will receive sunlight during peak daytime hours (usually between 9 a.m. and 3 p.m.) the concept of the "solar envelope" is used. This solar envelope identifies the area around the structure in which the collectors can be placed where no shadowing should occur during the specified time periods. Factors that need to be considered here are building height limitations, setback requirements (the minimum distance from the property line to any on-site structure including solar panels), vegetation, and neighboring buildings. Even the slope of the land can have an effect and must be considered when identifying the solar envelope of a particular building.

Problems of shade can be avoided by careful analysis of the envelope. A thorough analysis of the area must be conducted with solar sources in mind. If the collectors are to be raised above the roof surface, local zoning regulations on building height limitations should be consulted (these should be available from city hall or from county authorities). Likewise, if the collectors are to be placed somewhere in the yard, setback requirements, also in local zoning ordinances, will be important. It also is important to note neighboring structures and vegetation, particularly tall trees. If the solar collectors are to be placed relatively near someone else's property line, consideration must be given to the possibility of new construction on

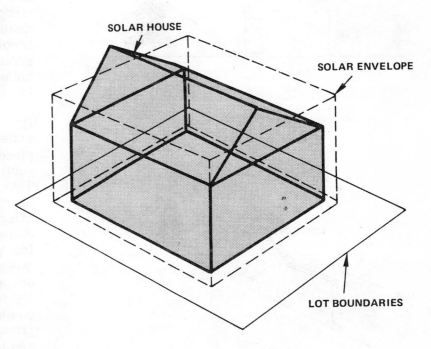

THE SOLAR ENVELOPE CAN BE HELPFUL IN DETERMINING POSSIBLE SHADING

that site or the growth of vegetation. If the next door neighbor decides that a new high-rise garage and a number of hardy pine trees would be nice additions to his or her property, a hastily mounted photovoltaic collector soon may be sitting in the shade.

Another important factor that also must be considered is the slope of the land. A shadow falling on a level surface will be of moderate length. However, a shadow falling on a downward sloped surface will be much longer, increasing in length as the slope increases in steepness. A tree or building on a hill some distance away could pose a potential shadowing problem, consequently this aspect also must be given special consideration when placing a solar collector.

In addition to using the solar envelope for deciding on where to place your solar collector, some other rules are useful: 1) try to place the solar collector on the northernmost section of the building (if practically feasible). This location will provide some assurance that neighboring structures or vegetation will not affect available sunlight. 2) Try to place the collector at or near the building height limitation for your area. This will again provide some measure of assurance that new construction will not affect your collector's performance. 3) site the collector as far away from vegetation as possible to prevent shading affects from future growth. It is important to remember that while you may be able to control the growth of plants and trees on your property, you may not be able to convince a neighbor or the city to cut off some interfering limbs.

You should give careful consideration to your solar collector location before making any

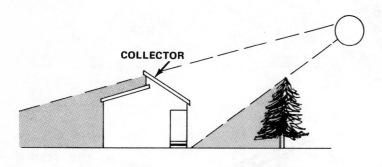

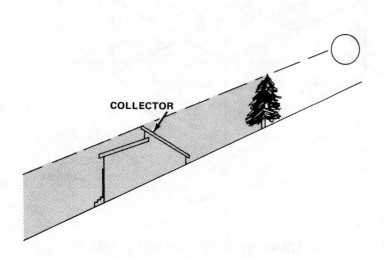

LONGER SHADOWS THAT CAN SHADE COLLECTORS ARE CAST ON SLOPES

final installation. A well thought out plan in the beginning should ensure many years of trouble free collector performance.

The Federal Role

The Federal government does not usually get involved in questions of solar rights and solar access. These issues generally are decided on the state and community level. The Federal government has, however, become involved in some significant ways, having passed many laws of major impact to the development of solar energy. One of these was the the Public Utilities Regulatory Policies Act passed in 1978 by the U.S. Congress. Among other things this act: 1) exempted small power producers, which would include residential photovoltaic systems, small hydroelectric plants, and other systems from most Federal utility regulations, 2) required electric utilities to interconnect with small power producers, and 3) required the utilities to pay a fair rate for the power purchased from the small power producers. In this act a small power producer is defined as one that does not produce more than 80 megawatts of electricity using alternative energy sources.

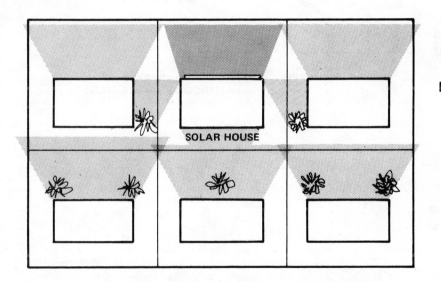

NEARBY BUILDINGS AND VEGETATION MAY SHADE YOUR PROPERTY

The Public Utilities Regulatory Policies Act (referred to as PURPA) has very important consequences for renewable energy system owners. Not only is a photovoltaic system (under 80 megawatts) exempt from confusing and complicated regulations that apply to large electric utilities, but they are recognized as legitimate sources of electricity that can even sell their excess electricity back to the

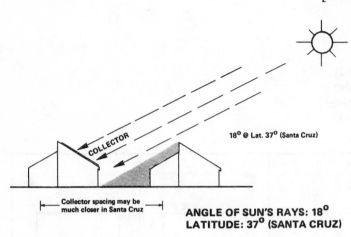

18° @ Lat. 37° (Santa Cruz)

COLLECTOR

Collector spacing may be
much closer in Santa Cruz

ANGLE OF SUN'S RAYS: 18°
LATITUDE: 37° (SANTA CRUZ)

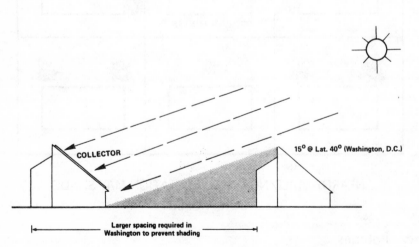

15° @ Lat. 40° (Washington, D.C.)

COLLECTOR

Larger spacing required in
Washington to prevent shading

ANGLE OF SUN'S RAYS: 15°
LATITUDE: 40° (WASHINGTON, D.C.)

GREATER DISTANCES ARE REQUIRED BETWEEN
BUILDINGS TO AVOID SHADING IN HIGHER
LATITUDES

power company. Some wind energy systems, and a few photovoltaic systems around the United States already are operating under the PURPA regulations and selling their excess electricity back to the utility. Additionally, residential owners of photovoltaic systems will be able to use the electric utility power for backup when the photovoltaic system does not produce enough energy. Solar Design Associates, builders of a photovoltaic residence in Carlisle, Massachusetts has predicted that the energy sold back to the utility by the photovoltaic system will compensate for energy bought from the utility producing a net annual electric bill of $0.00.

Other Federal activities in the solar area are primarily the responsibility of the U.S. Department of Energy (DOE). Much research into solar technologies has been conducted under DOE funding and some of the current operating systems can be attributed to DOE assistance. The Department of Energy efforts, however, have been undertaken as a support to the present and future photovoltaics industry. This industry, which has been growing at a rapid pace, has made significant contributions in the field of photovoltaics, many of which were independent of DOE assistance. It is this burgeoning industry that will be producing cost effective photovoltaic energy systems for residential use.

Questions of solar law do not usually fall under the auspices of either the DOE or the Federal Government. Legal issues concerning solar energy are primarily decided at the state or local level and it is at these levels of government that the most important questions are being considered.

State Activities

Many states have taken action to encourage the use of solar energy through financial incentives (see Chapter 8) and through legislation to remove obstacles and promote the use of solar systems. One area where a large number of states have taken action is in the regulation of electric utilities and in land use and zoning ordinances.

States generally keep close watch over public utilities through a State Public Utility Commission (PUC). These commissions determine how much the utility can charge its customers, how customers are to be charged, and whether or not the utility should build new plants. Some states already have established through their PUC's or the utilities themselves, progressive rate structures that encourage the use of solar energy. The State of Delaware, for instance, now has instituted a seasonal and peak use rate structure which more realistically reflects the actual cost of the energy being used by the customer. More traditional rate structures often do not charge what the energy actually costs the utility to produce. Through this and similar types of rate structures, electricity customers may find it more economical to reduce their energy consumption and install their own electricity generating system.

States also can influence the way land is used in local communities. Through what is known as "authorizing legislation," states can encourage local communities to plan solar communities and allow for adequate solar access ordinances. In some cases the state actually can mandate that land use plans be adopted that encourage solar energy use. Thus far, at least 25 states have taken action regarding land use policy to encourage solar energy systems. Some states, such as California, have taken very strong steps to protect solar access. California law now requires that "anyone who owns, occupies, or controls real estate is prohibited from allowing a tree or shrub to cast a shadow on a solar collector between 9:30 a.m. and 2:30 p.m." The California law also removes any local restrictions that might exist on the use of solar energy systems and requires that new housing subdivisions be designed to accommodate passive solar energy systems. In another example of state action, Oregon allows local governments to regulate solar access in zoning plans and subdivision regulations; private restrictions prohibiting solar energy systems are not permitted.

Local Activities

Many of the important legal issues surrounding solar rights questions are determined at the local level. It is at the local level where building codes are implemented, where zoning changes are made, and where disputes over solar access often are decided.

Generally, problems should not arise over installing a solar system on a house or building. However, because local ordinances were not devised with solar usage in mind, conflicts can arise. Further, some residential developments have established restrictive covenants governing the architecture and land use in the community. Most often questions will arise over solar access or architectural/aesthetic constraints. For an individual owning several acres of land, this may not be a problem, since they can site their collectors far enough away from neighboring property lines so as to remove any future possibility of interference with their access to the sun. It is areas of greater population density that present problems. If local or state ordinances do not explicitly outline individual solar rights, a neighbor whose tree casts a shadow on a solar collector may not be legally required to remove the tree.

There are several ways that unfavorable solar access situations can be avoided: 1) site the collector in such a way that it will not be shadowed during peak operating periods, 2) if not already provided for in local ordinances, request that community solar access rights be established, or 3) obtain an easement for solar access from adjacent property holders. An easement, simply stated, provides some sort of access to property not owned by the individual. In a typical example of an easement, a property owner whose property does not have direct access to a roadway because adjacent property owned by another individual separates him and the roadway, will be granted an easement to drive from the roadway to the enclosed property. Easements, when granted, usually are associated with the land and not the particular land owner, so that when the land over which an easement has been granted changes hands, the terms of the easement do not change (depending of course, on the length of the easement). In the case of solar access, an easement could be granted for the use of the sun's rays over adjacent property. Such an easement would then guarantee access to the solar energy and prevent any new construction or vegetation on the adjacent property from blocking the sunlight.

Zoning ordinances also are usually controlled at the local level. Before any new building can be constructed it must meet local zoning ordinances which often have a setback (how far from the property line the structure must be) and height requirement.

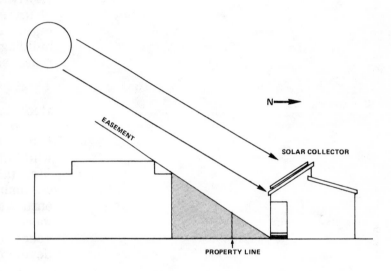

EASEMENTS CAN ENSURE SOLAR ACCESS

Also, additions to existing buildings must meet all zoning regulations. This sometimes can be a problem for solar systems that require unique building configurations which are not in compliance with the zoning code, and in order to be approved either a variance is provided (giving authorization for the structure even though it does not meet the zoning ordinance) or the zoning regulations need to be changed. Zoning provisions specifically oriented for solar systems are slowly finding their way into local codes. Recent changes in the Albuquerque, New Mexico, zoning regulations affecting height limitations on new buildings provided for secure solar access for reasonably located south walls.

Some communities have taken very strong steps to ensure solar access for new structures. The city of Port Arthur, Texas, now requires that all new homes be "sited to take advantage of solar energy," while also requiring that new subdivisions make plans to facilitate solar access. By taking action on a community-wide basis, such localities will be able to ensure solar access for all residents. It is expected that more communities in the future will be taking solar access considerations into account as they plan for new developments.

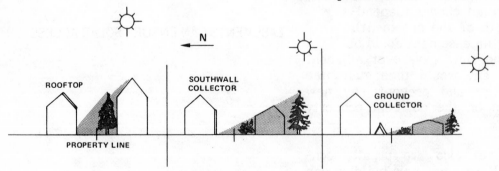

DIFFERENT COLLECTOR LOCATIONS WILL REQUIRE DIFFERENT HEIGHT LIMITATIONS

Building Codes

One final related area should also be noted: building codes. Building codes are issued so that new construction is done safely and with reliable components. These codes are used to ensure that electrical wiring will not cause fires, that plumbing is properly installed, and that proper building materials are used among other things. In many areas a new solar or photovoltaic system must meet these building codes before it will be approved for installation. Unfortunately, since photovoltaics are relatively new they are not mentioned specifically in any building codes nor in the National Electrical Code which is often cited as a local requirement. This leaves it up to the determination of the local authorities as to how photovoltaics should be evaluated in the building codes as written. In most cases the criteria are that the panels must be installed in a reasonably safe manner with adequate precautions taken for the possibility of fire, wind or storm damage and other circumstances. However, since photovoltaics are not yet mentioned specifically in the codes, they may be subjected to more stringent requirements than would otherwise be the case. A narrow interpretation of the code in regard to photovoltaics by the local code authorities could cause problems for those wanting to place the panels on a residential roof.

These problems, however, are in the process of being resolved. Work is going on, partly in cooperation with the DOE to revise the model building and electrical codes (these model codes usually are adopted by localities instead of creating all new ones for each city, town and state) so as to incorporate

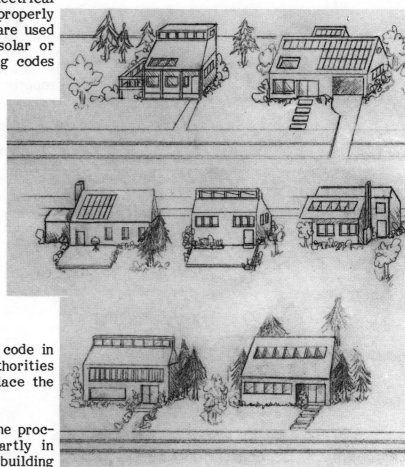

A WELL PLANNED SOLAR COMMUNITY WITH SOLAR ACCESS FOR EVERYONE

photovoltaics into their standards. Once this has been done, and local officials become aware of and familiar with these systems there should be no problem in receiving quick approval for your system.

So Those Are My Solar Rights

By now you should have at least a good notion of what constitutes one's "solar rights." While it has been shown that these rights are not guaranteed, careful planning can ensure adequate solar access for properly constructed solar systems. Further information can be obtained through many of the organizations listed in Appendix A or through the following groups: Environmental Policy Center, 317 Pennsylvania Avenue, N.W., Washington, D.C. 20003, the Institute for Local Self-Reliance, 1717 18th Street, N.W., Washington, D.C., 20009, or the Environmental Law Institute, 1346 Connecticut Avenue, N.W., Washington, D.C. 20036.

U.S. FEDERAL SOLAR LAWS

Public Law	Title	Date
93-409	Solar Heating and Cooling Demonstration Act of 1974	3 Sept. 74
93-438	Energy Reorganization Act of 1974	11 Oct. 74
93-473	Solar Energy Research, Development and Demonstration Act of 1974	26 Oct. 74
93-577	Federal Non-Nuclear Energy Research and Development Act of 1974	31 Dec. 74
94-385	Energy Conservation and Production Act	14 Aug. 76
95-88	International Development and Food Assistance Act of 1977	3 Aug. 77
95-91	Department of Energy Organization Act	4 Aug. 77
95-33	Youth Employment and Demonstration Projects Act of 1977	5 Aug. 77
95-113	Food and Agriculture Act of 1977	29 Sept. 77

U.S. FEDERAL SOLAR LAWS

Public Law	Title	Date
95-202	GI Bill Improvement Act of 1977	23 Nov. 77
95-238	Department of Energy Act of 1978 – Civilian Applications	25 Feb. 78
95-242	Nuclear Non-Proliferation Act of 1978	10 Mar. 78
95-253	National Sun Day — Joint Resolution	27 Mar. 78
95-315	Small Business Energy Loan Act	4 July 78
95-356	Military Construction Authorization Act, 1979	8 Sept. 78
95-424	International Development and Food Assistance Act of 1978	6 Oct. 78
95-426	Foreign Relations Authorization Act, Fiscal Year 1979	7 Oct. 78
95-476	Veterans' Housing Benefits Act of 1978	18 Oct. 78
95-557	Housing and Community Development Amendments of 1978	31 Oct. 78
95-577	Rayburn Office Building Solar Collector Installation	2 Nov. 78

U.S. FEDERAL SOLAR LAWS

Public Law	Title	Date
95–590	Solar Photovoltaic Energy Research, Development, and Demonstration Act of 1978	4 Nov. 78
96–223	Crude Oil Windfall Profit Tax Act	2 Apr. 80
96–294	Energy Security Act	30 June 80
96–310	Ocean Thermal Energy Conversion Research and Development Act of 1980	17 July 80
96–320	Ocean Thermal Energy Conversion Act of 1980	3 Aug. 80
96–345	Wind Energy Systems Act of 1980	8 Sept. 80

National Energy Act

95–617	Public Utility Regulatory Policies Act of 1978	9 Nov. 78
95–618	Energy Tax Act of 1978	9 Nov. 78
95–619	National Energy Conservation Policy Act	9 Nov. 78
95–620	Powerplant and Industrial Fuel Use Act of 1978	9 Nov. 78
95–621	Natural Gas Policy Act of 1978	9 Nov. 78

Note: Not included above (except for P.L. 95–238) are DOE and predecessor agency annual authorization and appropriation bills.

CHAPTER 8

Federal And State Solar
Tax Credits And Incentives

Introduction

In an effort to encourage the use of solar energy as an economical alternative to non-renewable fossil fuels, the federal government and many state governments have developed significant programs designed to assist the homeowner and small business person to purchase and use solar energy systems. The Federal government has approached this task primarily by offering tax credits to solar energy users. State programs are more varied, with many states offering a combination of low-interest loans, tax credits and deductions, and other measures. These programs have included both active and passive solar energy systems, although most government programs are designed to promote the use of active solar energy systems.

Federal Tax Credits —
Uncle Sam Gives a Helping Hand

The Federal government now allows qualified taxpayers to take up to a 40 percent credit toward their tax liability on up to the first $10,000 spent on solar thermal, wind, photovoltaic, or geothermal energy equipment purchased for home use since December 31, 1979. This $10,000 also can include the cost for the carpenter, electrician, or other technician to install the solar energy system on your home. This can mean that if you spend $10,000 on an installed system tomorrow, no matter where you live in the U.S., you can get a tax credit of $4,000. When you pay your federal taxes the solar system could end up costing you only $6,000 before you even consider any state or local assistance!

Like any program, there are some limitations on the federal tax credit. First of all, if you

---

**Residential
Federal Tax Credit**

$10,000 System Cost (Installed)
   x 40% Fed. Tax Credit
$ 4,000 Deducted from Federal Taxes
$ 6,000 Real Cost of System

**Business
Federal Tax Credit**

$5,000 System Cost (Installed)
  x 15% Business Tax Credit
$ 750 Deducted From Federal Taxes
$4,250 Real Cost of System

---

spend more than $10,000 on a solar system, you still can only get a maximum of $4,000 as a tax credit from the government. Secondly, the system you buy must be installed on your year-round home; vacation cabins are out. You also have to act in the next couple of years, since the program is funded only through 1985, and may not be continued past that time.

Yet even though there are some limitations to the federal tax credit, they are more than outweighed by the advantages. While the maximum credit may be limited to $4,000, a credit in excess of your tax liability in a given year can be carried over to subsequent years until 1987. In addition, this program offers a tax credit, not a deduction, which means you get the full $4,000, not some percentage of it based on your income level.

If you purchase a photovoltaic or other solar energy system, you can file for the credit with IRS Form 5695, entitled "Energy Credits," which is explained in the IRS publication number 903, called "Energy Credits for Individuals." If you need help filling it out, call your local Internal Revenue Service Office.*

As a business owner, you also may be entitled to a tax credit for the installation or purchase of a solar, geothermal, or wind energy system. The credit for businesses is not quite as impressive as the homeowners credit, since it is only for 15 percent of the costs, but it still helps bring the price down. This credit is similar to the residential credit, and also is available through 1985.

---

*For further information on all energy tax credits, contact the local IRS office, listed under the United States Government, Internal Revenue Service, "Tax Information" in your local telephone white pages.

The new (1980) Administration in the White House has pledged to continue the energy tax credits, even though other solar programs will be cut. Estimates from the Office of Management and the Budget (OMB) project that these credits will save homeowners and business people close to two and a half billion dollars between 1981 and 1986!

Other Help From Uncle Sam

Besides the tax credits, the Federal government has other programs which are designed to promote the use of solar energy systems. Under the National Energy Act, which was passed by Congress in 1980, Federal Housing Administration and Farmers Home Administration ceilings on insured mortages for single and multi-family homes were raised from $60,000 to $72,000 to cover the additional cost of solar or wind energy systems. Congress also granted the Veteran's Administration the authority to provide guarantees on loans for solar or other energy-related home improvements made at interest rates above home mortgage rates. The VA also can provide guarantees on loans for the purchase of homes equipped with solar devices.

In addition to these programs, the Department of Energy has a branch called the Office of Appropriate Technology.* This federal agency has the responsibility of encouraging the development and demonstration of new energy technologies that are appropriate to energy conservation and to the use of non-conventional energy resources (hence the name of the agency). Grants may be sought through this office to help design, and build small scale energy systems which will provide for local energy needs. These grants can

*There are ten regional offices of the Office of Appropriate Technology. To find the nearest office, please check Appendix A, under federal agencies.

be for as much as $50,000, and may be available to individuals, small businesses, local non-profit organizations and institutions, Indian tribes, and state and local government agencies.

Several other federal energy programs were authorized in the National Energy Conservation Policy Act (NECPA), passed by Congress in 1976. This act allows public utilities to make loans of up to $300 to their customers for the purchase and installation of solar equipment.* The NECPA also provides for grants to public and private schools and hospitals to pay for up to 50 percent (or up to 90 percent in hardship cases) of the cost of energy conservation projects. Photovoltaic power systems are included in this program, as they are in many federal energy programs.

States Get Into the Act Too

Almost every state by now has enacted some form of program to promote the use of solar energy in the home and in businesses. These programs include incentives in the reduction of excise taxes, property taxes, and state income taxes, as well as grant and loan projects, solar-oriented building codes and legislation and extensive information networks. Some examples of state programs include a Colorado law which allows for a state income tax deduction for the "total cost of installation, construction, reconstruction, remodeling, or acquisition of an alternative energy device," and a California law which would return half of the amount a builder invests in energy conservation equipment on homes he or she has built. Since the state programs vary greatly, check Appendix A for the Energy Office in your State.

*For more information on these loans, contact your local electric utility. Most utility companies have special energy information phone numbers to help you.

California Tax Credit

$5000 System Cost (Installed)
x 55% Tax Credit

$2750 Deducted From State Taxes

$2250 Real Cost of System

As an indication of what these federal and state programs can mean to you if you buy a photovoltaic system for your home, consider the following example. In Arizona, the state tax credit is 35 percent of the first $10,000. If this is coupled with the 40 percent federal credit on a purchase of a $2,500 system, the actual price of this system to you would only

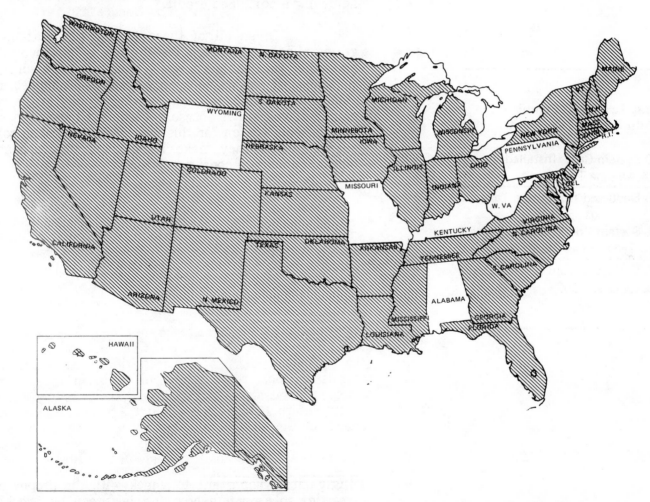

ALMOST EVERY STATE IN THE UNION HAS SOME FORM OF SOLAR TAX CREDIT

be $625. Most other states allow you to combine the federal and state tax credits in this manner. Only in California, Montana, and Massachusetts are the state credits reduced if the federal tax credit is also claimed; however, builders will sometimes pass the federal or state tax credit through to a home buyer who in turn may obtain the alternate credit thereby achieving a combined credit.*

Given all of these federal and state programs aimed at encouraging the use of photovoltaics and other renewable energy systems, it is no surprise that sales of renewable energy systems for homes and small businesses have been growing rapidly in the last couple of years. Of course government incentives are not the only reason for this increased interest in solar energy, but if they make it cheaper, they probably help to encourage consumer interest.

**Arizona Tax Credit Combined
With Federal Tax Credit**

$2,500 System Cost (Installed)
  x 35% Arizona Tax Credit

$ 875 Deducted from State Taxes
Plus
$2,500 System Cost (Installed)
  x 40% Federal Tax Credit

$1,000 Deducted from Federal Taxes
Total Real Cost: $625

---

*Again it is important to check with the proper authorities to ascertain how the laws can be properly applied to your situation.

STATE SOLAR TAX INCENTIVES

| State | Property Tax Exemption | Income Tax Credit | | Sales Tax Exemption |
		Deductible (%)	Maximum Deduction($)	
Alabama	—	—	—	—
Alaska	—	10%	$200	—
Arizona	yes	35%	$1000	yes
Arkansas	—	100%	no limit	—
California	—	55%	$3000	—
Colorado	yes	30%	$3000	—
Connecticut	*	—	—	yes
Delaware	—	—	$200*	—
Washington, DC	—	—	—	—
Florida	yes	—	—	yes
Georgia	*	—	—	refund
Hawaii	yes	10%	no limit	—
Idaho	—	100%	no limit	—
Illinois	yes	—	—	—
Indiana	yes	25%	$3000	—
Iowa	yes	—	—	—
Kansas	**	30%	$1500	—
Kentucky	—	—	—	—
Louisiana	yes	—	—	—
Maine	yes	20%	$100	refund
Maryland	yes+	—	—	—

STATE SOLAR TAX INCENTIVES

State	Property Tax Exemption	Income Tax Credit		Sales Tax Exemption
		Deductible (%)	Maximum Deduction($)	
Massachusetts	yes	35%	$1000	yes
Michigan	yes	25% – 15%	$1700	yes
Minnesota	yes	20%	$2000	—
Mississippi	—	—	—	limited
Missouri	—	—	—	—
Montana	yes	5% – 2.5%	$125	—
Nebraska	—	—	—	refund
Nevada	limited	—	—	—
New Hampshire	*	—	—	—
New Jersey	yes	—	—	yes
New Mexico	—	25%	$1000***	—
New York	yes	—	—	—
North Carolina	yes	25%	$1000	—
North Dakota	yes	5%	no limit	—
Ohio	yes	10%	$1000	yes
Oklahoma	—	+	—	no
Oregon	yes	25%	$1000	—
Pennsylvania	—	—	—	—
Rhode Island	yes	10%	$1000	—
South Carolina	—	25%	$1000	—
South Dakota	yes	—	—	—

STATE SOLAR TAX INCENTIVES

State	Property Tax Exemption	Income Tax Credit		Sales Tax Exemption
		Deductible (%)	Maximum Deduction($)	
Tennessee	yes	—	—	—
Texas	yes	—	—	—
Utah	no	10%	$1000	—
Vermont	*	25%	$1000	—
Virginia	*	—	—	—
Washington	yes	—	—	—
West Virginia	—	—	—	—
Wisconsin	yes	—	no#	—
Wyoming	—	—	—	—

*local option
**partial refund
***heating and cooling only
#direct rebate
+sliding scale based on % of federal credit
*for water heating systems only
+credit at local option

This data is accurate as of January 1980, check with state officials to determine the present law. In some states, such as Arizona, where a 35 percent tax credit is available, total tax credits go as high as 75 percent of total system cost. Applying this credit to a system that costs $1000 would give a return of $750, making the actual system cost only $250.

In 1980, Bob and Mary Brown spent $3,000 for a solar photovoltaic system on their principal home (renewable energy source costs). All items were installed during 1980.

The renewable energy source credit is 40% of the first $10,000 spent (limited to a credit of $4,000). Their credit for renewable energy source costs is $1,200 (40% x $3,000).

The Brown's Form 1040 shows a tax of $1,895 on line 37 which they reduce by credits of $275 (lines 38 through 44, Form 1040) leaving a tax of $1,620. They may use their total credit of $1,200 because it is less than their tax. The Brown's Form 5695, Energy Credits, is provided as an example.

In future years the Browns may take a credit of up to $7,000 more renewable energy source costs for this home ($10,000 maximum amount minus $3,000 costs in 1980) for a total available credit of $2,800 (40% of $7,000).

Form **5695** Department of the Treasury Internal Revenue Service	**Energy Credits** ▶ Attach to Form 1040. ▶ See Instructions on back.	19**80** 34

Name(s) as shown on Form 1040   BOB AND MARY BROWN   Your social security number 111 11 1111

Enter in the space below the address of your principal residence on which the credit is claimed if it is different from the address shown on Form 1040.

Part I Fill in your energy conservation costs (but do not include repair or maintenance costs).
If you have an energy credit carryover from a previous tax year and no energy savings costs this year, skip to Part III, line 16.

A. Answer the following question: Was your principal residence substantially completed before April 20, 1977? . . . ☑ Yes ☐ No
B. If you checked the "NO" box, you CANNOT claim an energy credit for conservation cost. Do NOT fill in lines 1 through 7 of this form.

1 Energy Conservation Items:			
a Insulation	1a		
b Storm (or thermal) windows or doors . . .	1b		
c Caulking or weatherstripping	1c		
d A furnace replacement burner that reduces the amount of fuel used	1d		
e A device for modifying flue openings to make a heating system more efficient	1e		
f An electrical or mechanical furnace ignition system that replaces a gas pilot light . . .	1f		
g A thermostat with an automatic setback	1g		
h A meter that shows the cost of energy used	1h		
2 Total (add lines 1a through 1h)	2		
3 Maximum amount	3	$2,000	00
4 Enter the total energy conservation costs for this residence from your 1978 and 1979 Form 5695, line 2 .	4		
5 Subtract line 4 from line 3 (If line 4 is more than line 3, do not complete any more of this part. You cannot claim any more energy conservation credit for this residence.)	5		0
6 Enter the amount on line 2 or line 5, whichever is less	6		
7 Enter 15% of line 6 here and include in amount on line 15 below	7		

Part II Fill in your renewable energy source costs (but do not include repair or maintenance costs).
If you have an energy credit carryover from a previous tax year and no energy savings costs this year, skip to Part III, line 16.

8 Renewable Energy Source Items:			
a Solar	8a	3,000	00
b Geothermal	8b		
c Wind	8c		
9 Total (add lines 8a through 8c)	9	3,000	00
10 Maximum amount	10	$10,000	00
11 Enter the total renewable energy source costs for this residence from your 1978 Form 5695, line 5 and 1979 Form 5695, line 9	11		
12 Subtract line 11 from line 10 (If line 11 is more than line 10, do not complete any more of this part. You cannot claim any more renewable energy source cost credit for this residence.)	12	10,000	00
13 Enter amount on line 9 or line 12, whichever is less	13	3,000	00
14 Enter 40% of line 13 here and include in amount on line 15 below	14	1,200	00

Part III Fill in this part to figure the limitation

15 Add line 7 and line 14. If less than $10, enter zero	15	1,200	00
16 Enter your energy credit carryover from a previous tax year	16	0	00
17 Add lines 15 and 16	17	1,200	00
18 Enter the amount of tax shown on Form 1040, line 37	18	1,895	00
19 Add lines 38 through 44 from Form 1040 and enter the total	19	275	00
20 Subtract line 19 from line 18. If zero or less, enter zero	20	1,620	00
21 Residential energy credit. Enter the amount on line 17 or line 20, whichever is less. Also, enter this amount on Form 1040, line 45	21	1,200	00

A SAMPLE FEDERAL ENERGY TAX CREDIT FORM

CHAPTER 9

Your Opportunities In Photovoltaics

Photovoltaics — A Challenge in Your Future

In previous chapters, we have discussed various aspects of photovoltaics: how and why it works, how it is used in an energy system, what it is used for today, how the law affects its use, and how the government might help the buyer. In all of this, we have approached the reader as someone who wants to become familiar with photovoltaics, and possibly use it as a reliable energy source. But as you have read this book and pondered its implications, you may come to the realization that other opportunities exist besides the direct use of photovoltaics. There are a host of other opportunities in photovoltaics. These opportunities could include expanding intellectual horizons, broadening professional capabilities, increasing your trade skills, changing your career or entering a new field as a pioneer in the development of solar energy.

You may have one or many reasons for being interested in photovoltaics. Many people see solar energy as a more environmentally benign means of producing energy than current polluting energy sources such as coal and oil. For instance, it has been estimated that, with equal power production, a coal plant will 1) produce over 62 times more air-borne particulate pollution; 2) spread pollution over a much larger area, affecting up to 1,000 times as many people; 3) over a twenty-year lifetime necessitate the use of over four times as much land for power production, and 4) produce over five times as much thermal pollution (discharge of steam and hot water into the air and rivers). For these reasons, and others, people who want economic growth, but also desire a liveable environment are turning to photovoltaics.

(COURTESY SPIRE CORPORATION)

HIGH PERFORMANCE PHOTOVOLTAIC MODULES

Some individuals see opportunities in the photovoltaics field as a means of upgrading and enhancing their professional skills. Whether one is an electrician, a bank clerk, a physicist, or in another occupation, photovoltaics and other solar technologies will have an impact on your life in the years to come.

Many people see the next several years as the time to prepare for this future. More and more colleges and universities are offering courses and degrees in solar engineering design, financing, economics and other areas. Continuing education courses and training seminars are being conducted to provide professionals with the skills and knowledge necessary to keep abreast of this rapidly growing field. People are told constantly to save for the future; some are taking this advice a step further by assuring that their capabilities will keep up with the times.

Other people may seek opportunities in the photovoltaics field because they do not want to work at jobs which offer little satisfaction. Numerous studies have been performed in recent years which indicate that many people in today's job environment get little pleasure from their work and consequently have little pride in their job. Whether as a result of feeling lost in a massive corporation, or for other reasons, many individuals are seeking opportunities in new environments. Photovoltaics is one of these new environments which promises a variety of new opportunities--it is one of the challenging new frontiers of the future. The field of photovoltaics offers the challenge of a new industry moving into uncharted regions. It offers the challenge of making history, not following the bureaucracy. It offers reasons for pride in one's work. It offers opportunities with a purpose.

One does not need any specific type of life philosophy or world view in order to become involved in the field of photovoltaics; the opportunities are so numerous and varied that anyone can find good cause to pursue new challenges in photovoltaics.

To give you an idea of the scope of the photovoltaics field in the near future, let's take a look at a scenario which has been forecast by both government agencies, and private forecasting organizations.

Looking Toward a Solar Future

A recent U.S. government study concluded that the solar industries could generate as many as three to five million new jobs in the U.S. alone by the turn of the century. These jobs would be almost entirely newly created positions; they would not displace current workers as would the expansion of other energy technologies. While the total includes employees associated with all the solar technologies, e.g. wind energy, solar thermal, biomass and photovoltaics, somewhere around half of these people would be involved to some degree in the photovoltaics field. To put this projection into perspective, the lower end of this estimate represents more people than are currently employed by all of the agencies of the U.S. government! The types of jobs involved will include semi-skilled and skilled workers, scientists and other technical personnel, tradesmen, sales people, and many others. To understand the myriad of opportunities that are possible, lets take a detailed look at photovoltiacs, at each stage from the mining of raw silicon, to the operation of a utility owned photovoltaic system.

Imagine the year is 1990 or thereabouts. You are at the receiving dock of an integrated photovoltaics manufacturing facility. Arriving at the gate are raw materials which will be used to produce photovoltaic arrays. Quartz arrives in freight trains, and trucks arrive with glass and assorted types of

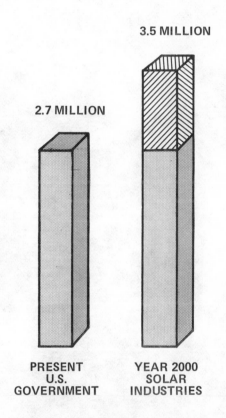

A COMPARISON OF EMPLOYMENT IN SOLAR INDUSTRIES AND THE U.S. GOVERNMENT

plexiglass which will be used to encapsulate the photo-voltaic arrays. Aluminum, steel, wood, and other plastics also are unloaded, to be used in the frames and supporting structures of the photovoltaic panels. All of these materials have been produced by newly hired personnel in these recently invigorated traditional industries to satisfy the nation's demand for photovoltaic power systems.

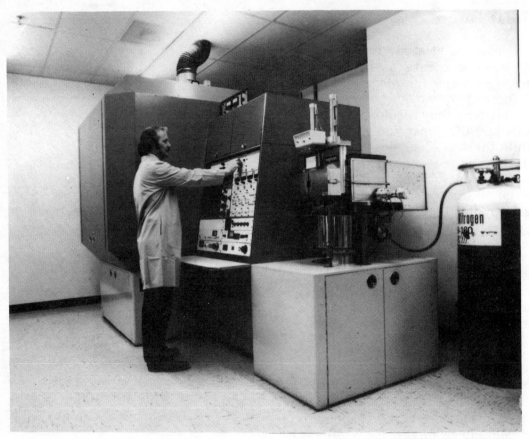

(COURTESY SPIRE CORPORATION)

JOBS WILL INCLUDE THE OPERATION OF SOPHISTICATED PRODUCTION EQUIPMENT

After watching the unloading of materials for a short time, you venture into the production facility to watch the manufacturing of the photovoltaic panels. It is a highly automated operation, but there still are skilled workers and technicians overseeing the production line. In an adjacent space are physicists, engineers, and chemists researching new, innovative ways to produce photovoltaics at lower costs and with less material. You notice that almost nothing is wasted in this production operation; waste material is recycled automatically under the watchful eyes of the quality control managers and engineers. Production engineers are to the side of the production area, running some tests on a new piece of equipment which was developed specifically for the high speed and efficient production of photovoltaic panels.

You also notice that there are several different materials and processes being used to produce the photovoltaic cells; a number of independent laboratories and university research groups have contributed beneficial results on cell physics, design, and processing optimization.

(COURTESY SPIRE CORPORATION)

TECHNICAL PERSONNEL WILL BE REQUIRED IN ALL
PHASES OF PV PRODUCTION

(COURTESY SPIRE CORPORATION)

TECHNICIAN TESTING ELECTRICAL CHARACTERISTICS OF SOLAR CELLS

Outside, in the management offices, the sales and marketing staffs are busy selling next month's photovoltaics production. Managers, company executives, accountants, secretaries, and a variety of other administrative personnel are busy keeping the business end of this operation functioning smoothly. Venturing outside to the shipping docks, you see workers busily loading finished photovoltaic panels into trucks for shipment to wholesale distributors and facilities, called "systems houses" which take the panels and incorporate them into standardized photovoltaic power systems.

You hop aboard one of the trucks bound for a "systems house," and upon arrival, again find an active receiving dock, where batteries, and other storage medium and power handling components, are arriving. This "systems house" is a small business, assembling photovoltaic systems for the local market. There are a number of similar business concerns throughout the country, some are large, mass distribution services, others are producers of photovoltaic systems in small quantities for local or specialized markets. As in the photovoltaic manufacturing facility, you see production workers, technicians, engineers, and other technical staff designing and assembling photovoltaic systems. In another room are architects, electrical, structural and mechanical engineers, and people at drafting tables designing systems for specialized applications. Assisting these professionals are students on summer internships, or working as part of their education.

In the offices of this small business, a company executive is busy discussing financing arrangements with a photovoltaics specialist at the bank. Another is arranging insurance for a system to be installed with an insurance underwriter who specializes in photovoltaics and other solar insurance. The treasurer of the company is discussing a business venture with a security analyst whose specialty is stocks of solar companies.

To find out where these photovoltaic systems are being sold, you hop aboard another truck, this one bound for a local "energy store." At this small retail outlet, very similar to a hardware store but specializing in alternative energy and energy conservation products, the owner is showing a prospective buyer information on a small photovoltaic system. He indicates that it has been tested by an independent testing laboratory, and that it meets and exceeds all applicable consumer product standards. The potential buyer wants to install the system on his vacation cabin in the mountains, which is far from any electric power lines. He has checked with the local building inspector and with a local architect who specializes in passive and active solar building; both have indicated that the system can be incorporated into the cabin's roof.

The customer seems satisfied with the system, and he leaves to arrange the financing with the local bank. Financial analysts at the bank have no trouble providing him with a small loan (systems are not that expensive), especially after he tells them that

Types of Organizations Involved in Photovoltaics

Large Corporations

- Energy development firms
- Semiconductor manufacturers
- Electronic component manufacturers
- Utilities
- Aerospace firms
- National testing laboratories
- Photovoltaics manufacturers

Small Businesses

- Wholesale outlets
- Retail stores
- Local financial institutions
- Architectural firms
- HVAC installers
- Trucking companies
- Engineering/system integration firms

Government/Nonprofit Organizations

- Government research laboratories
- Government regulatory agencies
- Consumer action groups
- Solar lobbying groups
- Energy extension services
- Government solar information services

Education and Research

- Colleges
- Universities

a real estate agent has informed him that adding the photovoltaic system to the remote cabin will enhance the value of this property.

Being an electrician by trade, and in addition boasting some skill as a carpenter, the owner of the new photovoltaic system sets about to install it on his cabin. He knows that his rights to the sunlight striking the panels will be assured, since the solar rights of the homeowner are protected in his area by strong solar laws. And he also knows that with proper installation, the system will meet local building and zoning codes, since they have been changed in the last couple of years to allow unrestricted use of photovoltaics on most buildings. His wife is concerned with air and water pollution, being a lawyer in consumer affairs, and supports the decision to use nonpolluting solar energy.

The customer also knows that if he decides to buy a new home in the coming years, he probably will not have to buy a separate photovoltaic system for the house, since there are many architectural and construction firms which specialize in building homes which incorporate photovoltaics into solar homes in combination with solar hot water, space heating and cooling, heat storage media in the walls, and passive solar architecture to maximize the heating and cooling effects of the sun.

If you take a jaunt over to the local electric utility you will find more career opportunities in the photovoltaics field. This utility has a photovoltaic division which is responsible for both their large array fields and house-mounted arrays. Rather than buy from the system house, the utility assembles its own systems, buying the panels direct from the manufacturer. Besides the project managers, operators, systems analysts and engineers, this division employees electricians, a maintenance staff, and a legal counsel specializing in solar law.

(COURTESY MIT LINCOLN LABORATORY)

WORKERS WILL BE NEEDED FOR THE INSTALLATION
OF PV PANELS

Winding up this short journey please note that is was not meant to indicate that the purchase of a photovoltaic system will be a complicated affair; rather, it will typically be no more complicated than the purchase of an air conditioning system or other large equipment for the home or business. But from manufacture to the final end use, a host of individuals will have some impact on the photovoltaic system. With the large-scale use of photovoltaics or any other solar technology, numerous workers will be involved with specialized skills and capabilities in solar energy in their respective fields.

But very few individuals with these skills presently are available. For example, it is expected that the solar fields will require around half a million skilled professionals in a variety of occupations by 1990. In 1978, there were slightly over 22,000 people working full or part time in the solar energy field. But the field is growing rapidly, with projections of close to 100,000 people involved in solar energy by 1983. The rapid growth experienced by the photovoltaics industry in the last several years indicates that photovoltaics will assume a larger and larger share of the total involvement in solar energy fields.

The next few years will be a particularly good time for people to enter the photovoltaics field,

(COURTESY MIT LINCOLN LABORATORY)

INSTALLATION OF PV PANELS

and become part of this dynamic growth. There will be many different avenues one can take to enter the photovoltaics field. Which approach is best will depend ultimately on the preferences of the individual.

The Road to Solar

Many organizations are involved in solar energy. The following kinds of organizations will be heavily involved in the photovoltaics field in the years ahead:

Large Corporations: A number of major corporations are currently working in the photovoltaics field, or investigating future involvement. These firms include those in the fields of energy development, semiconductors, electronic components, electricity production, and consumer products. Most of these firms are approaching photovoltaics as manufacturers, since they typically have the research and development organization, and mass production technology which are necessary for high volume production of photovoltaic modules. A number of major international oil companies have initiated photovoltaics manufacturing subsidiaries in order to diversify into other energy fields.

The attributes of large corporations as employers include such factors as large capital resources and research budgets for development work, established marketing structures, pension plans and other benefits, and usually very competitive salaries and promotion potential. Many people enjoy working for a large organization because of the availability of resources, specialization of manpower, and other tangible and intangible benefits. On the other hand, some people may find drawbacks in working for a large diversified business. Negative aspects may include a feeling of being overwhelmed by the immensity of the firm, or specialization which is required on the job to the point of having no real concept of the final product of a project, or impersonal relations with superiors.

Small Businesses: For those people who, for one reason or another, do not want to work in a large organization, there will be many different types of small businesses involved in photovoltaics. Retail and wholesale outlets will be marketing photovoltaic systems. Local trucking firms will be delivering materials and finished systems. Construction and maintenance firms, probably working on the local level, will install and maintain photovoltaic systems. Consulting firms such as architectural and engineering firms, research organizations, training firms, and others, will supply services on local, regional, national and international levels.

Of course there are drawbacks to working for a small business. Job security may not be as reliable as with larger organizations. While the failure rate for small businesses in the solar field is not significantly different than the rate for small businesses in general, the small business failure rate often is relatively high. One of the major causes of small business failure is a lack of understanding of routine business operations on the part of the owner or executive officer. If you decide to work in a small business, or more importantly, to start your own, you must be sure that the business end of the operation is fully understood. There are a number of books available which are designed to help the small business.

Working for or owning a small business can offer the opportunities to develop a broad range of skills and not to be confined to a highly specialized area. It also can provide a work environment which may be less structured than larger organizations; in the case of your own business, you decide when to work, and how much to work. Working for a small company also provides the opportunity to undertake a

(COURTESY MIT LINCOLN LABORATORY)

BDM CORPORATION PHOTOVOLTAIC SYSTEM AT MIT LINCOLN LABORATORY SOUTHWEST RESIDENTIAL EXPERIMENT STATION

project with many facets, rather than only one part of the overall task. Finally, as part of a small business, the individual often can make a significant impact on policies and performance which can provide tremendous personal satisfaction and pride in one's work.

(COURTESY MIT LINCOLN LABORATORY)

PHOTOVOLTAIC TEST HOUSE AT THE FLORIDA SOLAR ENERGY CENTER

Government and Nonprofit Organizations: For those interested in working outside the private profit-making sector, government agencies and nonprofit institutions offer many opportunities. Government agencies at all levels will be regulating, providing testing services, undertaking research, and performing many other functions in the photovoltaics field. For instance, in the U.S., the Department of Energy maintains five energy laboratories and also regional solar centers to provide information and research into various solar technologies. Nonprofit organizations, such as the Solar Lobby, provide information to consumers and support photovoltaics in many other ways.

These organizations may offer the individual opportunities which may not be available in a private company. Working to promote the public good, or to support consumer interests can be a very rewarding occupation. By the same token, working for one of these organizations in many cases offers the opportunity to become involved in legislation, consumer advocacy, or a host of other areas in which private firms usually do not get involved. Government agencies, especially research laboratories such as Sandia Laboratories in New Mexico, or the Massachusetts Institute of Technology's Lincoln Laboratories, have resources available which may not be available to small businesses or other organizations.

Education and Research: Another form of opportunity is available to the photovoltaics advocate in the areas of research and education. A variety of

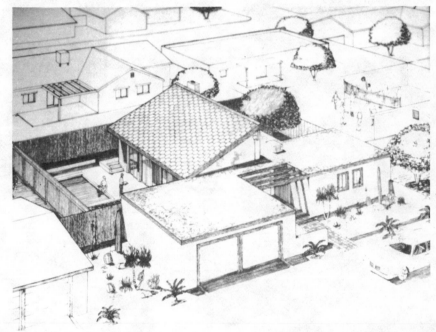

(COURTESY GENERAL ELECTRIC CORPORATION)

PROTOTYPE PHOTOVOLTAIC HOUSE

institutions of higher learning offer opportunities in teaching, researching, or learning about photovoltaics and other solar technologies. For the teacher or researcher, these institutions offer an academic environment in which to pursue areas of interest. They also offer a means of disseminating information to others, in undergraduate and graduate work, and in the form of continuing education.

The intention of this passage was to indicate some of the places to go for a profession or business in photovoltaics. But few people are trained or knowledgeable about how to identify these opportunities. The question so often raised is, where do you start?

AERIAL VIEW OF THE FLORIDA SOLAR ENERGY CENTER

(COURTESY MIT LINCOLN LABORATORY)

How to Start

There are a number of ways to familiarize yourself with the photovoltaics job market or with educational opportunities offered in the field. Some of these means are:

1. Check with local universities, colleges, and community schools. More and more schools, especially on the local level, are offering courses in subjects from general solar energy to solar architecture or economics. The National Solar Energy Education Directory,* compiled by the Solar Energy Research Institute (SERI), lists solar courses and curricula at over 700 institutions throughout the U.S. If a course on solar energy could be useful for your present job skills, see if your employer will share the cost.

2. Contact people in the field. State Energy Offices, your Congressman or Congresswoman, or local nonprofit environmental or energy organizations may be able to provide information. The Citizen's Energy Directory** published by the Citizen's Energy Project (see Appendix A) lists government and nonprofit organizations and other sources of information or contacts in the field.

3. Check with trade or professional organizations. With many trades expanding into the solar energy field, and with greater contact between many professions and aspects of solar energy, the national associations are developing contact information which may be of use.

*Available from Superintendent of Documents, U.S. Government Printing Office, Washington, D.C. as stock number 061-000-000210-3.

**1413 K Street, NW, Washington, D.C. 20005. Published in 1978, the directory sells for $7.50.

4. Visit a local energy store which carries conservation and renewable energy products and services. If they cannot help you, there may be product literature which will provide names of companies or individuals in the field.

5. If a particular area interests you, get one of the books listed in the chapters of this publication. NASA publishes a continuing bibliography on energy which covers a wide range of government and nonprofit funded publications on energy in general and photovoltaics in particular.*

6. Visit an energy exhibit or conference. These conferences and exhibits are taking place with increasing frequency and are a terrific source of personal contact with representatives of firms in the solar fields. Most solar periodicals have a listing of upcoming events.

7. Check the library for a listing of solar products manufacturers. Several organizations publish guides to the solar products of companies. These publications include The Solar Age Solar Products Specifications Guide**, and The Solar Census.***

---

*Available from the National Technical Information Service (NTIS), Springfield, Virginia 22161 for $15 in the U.S., $30 outside the U.S.

**Available from Solar Age, Harrisville, New Hampshire 03450. $165.00 pays for the guide and six bimonthly updates.

***Available from Aatec Publications, P.O. Box 7119, Ann Arbor, MI 48107 (313)-663-3424. $45.00 for the 500-page guide.

8. Check the library or newsstand for solar magazines, including <u>Solar Age</u>, <u>Solar Engineering</u> and <u>Alternative Sources of Energy</u>. MONEGON also publishes a bimonthly journal entitled the "Solar Photovoltaics Monitor." These periodicals can provide information on developments, businesses and conferences in photovoltaics.

9. If you are interested in starting your own business, the Small Business Administration (SBA) can offer invaluable assistance. Also, check with your local Chamber of Commerce for pertinent information on local resources.

There are many other possible sources of information (see Appendix A) that may help you to locate opportunities in the photovoltaic field. There is a whole new field of challenges to be found. If you are a student, now may be the time to begin to prepare for your post-graduate career. If you are employed and looking for more excitement or personal satisfaction from the job, perhaps now is the time to find the sun in your future!

MODEL OF GENERAL ELECTRIC
RESIDENTIAL PROTOTYPE

(COURTESY GENERAL ELECTRIC CORPORATION)

CHAPTER 10

Epilogue —
The Future Of Photovoltaics

Introduction

In earlier chapters, we discussed some of the many current uses of photovoltaics. But these are just the tip of the proverbial iceberg. Both the variety of applications and the number of users will increase dramatically in the next ten years. Many factors are at work to account for this: the reduction in the cost of photovoltaics, the increasing cost of conventional fuels, and the increasing interest in photovoltaics on the part of government agencies, business leaders, and other consumers.

Photovoltaics will be used around the world; there are virtually no locations where some use of photovoltaics will not be practical. Photovoltaic systems will be used for electrification of isolated villages in developing and developed countries. Photovoltaic systems will be used on "energy farms" to produce hydrogen fuels, and will be used in space to power satellites, space stations, and manned exploratory missions. Photovoltaics will be used in large, central generating facilities, as well as used in small, decentralized applications.

This chapter is designed to tell you a little bit about the future use of photovoltaics. Because the photovoltaic field is in an early stage of development, no one can predict exactly its future evolution. What we present here are our projections of the future based on knowledge of the current technology, and an informed understanding of where it is heading.

Village Electrification

In the future, photovoltaics will be used to bring a measure of prosperity to the tens of thousands of isolated villages in the developing countries of the world. In so doing, photovoltaic power systems will raise the meager standard of living of many of these people and help establish strong agricultural and cottage industries as a basis for further economic growth.

In many countries around the world, there currently is no reliable nationwide electricity generating capacity. Although most nations have a central electric utility generating power for homes and businesses in the major cities, many isolated villages are not connected to the utility grid. Most people in the industrialized countries forget how much we rely on electricity to meet our basic needs. But without electrification, these villages may have inadequate lighting, there may not be any refrigeration for the storage of perishable foods and medicines, and drinkable water may be difficult to obtain.

Some isolated villages have been using diesel generators to provide small quantities of electricity; however, this arrangement can be costly and maintenance problems occur frequently. Other villages have been connected to the central utility grid by power lines stretched over many miles of often very rough terrain. While interconnection provides a more reliable power supply than diesel engines, it also involves an expense which in many cases is prohibitively high. Installation of stand-alone photovoltaic systems in these isolated regions will literally "shed some light" on the problem of rural electrification.

The cost in time, effort, and resources involved in the use of photovoltaics, in an increasing number of situations, is less than that required for the installation and operation of diesel generators or extended power lines. In villages in the developing

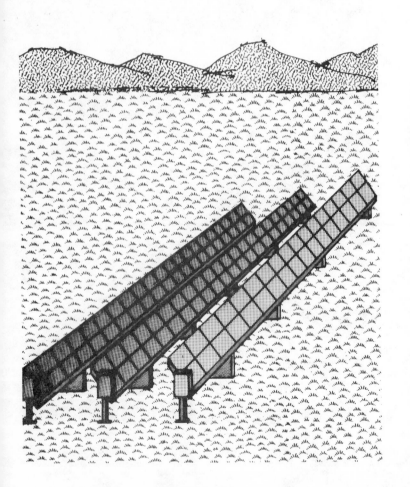

ARRAY FIELD

countries, photovoltaic panels will be mounted on rooftops or on unused parcels of land adjacent to the village, to provide electrification as is needed. Fortunately, in the isolated areas of many developing nations, particularly in regions with more sunlight, unused land is plentiful and can be obtained without displacing homes, businesses, or crop land.

The use of photovoltaic systems will be of great importance to many countries as they work to develop their economies and to provide for the needs of their citizens. In an isolated village in the future, a photovoltaic power system will supply electricity to operate irrigation pumps, hence greatly increasing local food production. Electricity from the photovoltaic system also will provide power for refrigeration of the perishable foods and medicines that are needed to keep the residents healthy. Lighting will be supplied to schools, medical facilities, and community centers. Photovoltaics will make it possible to install communications equipment, including radios and television sets, in order to provide a link to the rest of the country and the world through news, information, and educational programming. Once photovoltaic systems are installed to provide rural electrification, an almost endless list of uses are possible that will greatly improve the health and standard of living of the citizens of these countries. Installations in Africa, and even in the U.S., (see Chapter 2) already have shown the effectiveness of photovoltaics in this application.

Hydrogen Production with Photovoltaics

Photovoltaics is the only solar technology which produces electricity directly from the sun. Photovoltaics also produces electricity more directly than any conventional technology. Oil, for example, must be burned to produce heat, which in turn is applied to water to produce steam, which in turn is used to drive turbines, which finally produce electricity. Because photovoltaics generate electricity so simply, it often is assumed that photovoltaics will only be used to produce electricity, without providing power in other forms. But another use of photovoltaics has been proposed by a German physicist, Dr. Reinhard Dahlberg: the use of photovoltaics to produce hydrogen.

Hydrogen has been demonstrated to be an ideal fuel for a variety of uses. It is transportable by pipeline, ship, or tanker trucks. It already has been proved as an effective fuel for transportation vehicles, and for a number of industrial uses. Hydrogen can be stored for use at a later time, or can be used as a storage medium for electricity, to be burned to produce electricity during non-sunlight hours. Hydrogen is virtually pollution free, the only emission from combustion being water.

While the use of photovoltaics to produce hydrogen is not a well publicized process, it is a relatively simple technique. Almost everyone is familiar with the chemical equation for water, H_2O. Water consists of two atoms of hydrogen (H_2) and one atom of oxygen (O). Using the electrolysis process, hydrogen atoms can be separated from the oxygen atom and collected as pure hydrogen gas. The electrolysis process, and the separation of the hydrogen and oxygen atoms, results from the application of electricity to water. This electricity can be provided directly by photovoltaics.

ARTIST'S CONCEPTION OF A PHOTOVOLTAIC/ HYDROGEN PRODUCTION FACILITY

Hydrogen could be produced on a massive scale on "energy farms," or large expanses of uninhabited, unused land where water is abundant or to which water could be pumped, and which has a significant amount of daily solar insolation. These "farms" would be filled with large photovoltaic array fields, which will produce electricity. This electricity would be conducted into electrolysis tanks filled with water. The hydrogen gas produced through electrolysis would be stored in a large storage system, for transportation to population centers or to industrial facilities. The hydrogen also may be reserved for conventional turbine production of electricity at night or on cloudy days.

Hydrogen "farms" provide an environmentally benign alternative to the current use of polluting hydrocarbon fuels. The energy farms would be located in relatively isolated areas, away from population centers, so they would not present any dangers in case of accident. Hydrogen is a pure fuel, without contaminants, and its combustion produces only water. Photovoltaics is the ideal power source for these farms. The use of photovoltaics also is nonpolluting, and large array fields can be erected in isolated areas, since they would not need to be located close to fuel supplies, and require very little operational and maintenance support.

In concept, the production of hydrogen with photovoltaics is very attractive. There are several aspects of this proposal which require further research and development. Hydrogen storage techniques must be further refined before they can be used economically on a large scale. Large (many thousands of kilowatts) photovoltaic array fields must be built, which will require a large investment of money and land. But hydrogen farms hold the promise of an almost unlimited supply of readily useable fuel in our future.

Photovoltaics in Central Systems

While photovoltaics is ideal for smaller, distributed power systems, it also can be used in the generation of electricity from central sources similar to the power plants currently used by the electric utilities. Even with the advent of readily available, low-cost residential photovoltaic systems, centralized generating facilities still will make a significant contribution to meeting our electricity needs. Large-scale photovoltaic systems will be used to supplement, and may eventually replace many of the conventionally fueled power plants currently in use by most utilities.

The construction, fuel, and maintenance costs of conventional power plants have been rising rapidly in recent years. The cost and time presently needed for the building of a nuclear power plant can run over several billion dollars and take ten or twelve years, respectively. These costs are becoming prohibitively expensive, even to large utilities. As the cost of these new facilities continues to increase, the cost of a large photovoltaic system over its lifetime will make it cost competitive with conventional methods of large-scale power generation. These photovoltaic power stations could range in size from several hundred to several thousand kilowatts, depending on the available land, electricity requirements, and the amount of sunlight available in the region.

The use of photovoltaics also may lead to the development of more localized utilities. Cities and large towns may have their own photovoltaic systems supplemented by conventional hydro, coal, or nuclear power plants. These towns could incorporate a combination of large photovoltaic array fields, and smaller roof or ground mounted systems using space on or near offices, homes, shopping centers, and farms. A variety of different size arrays would be integrated into the utility grid, and the electricity generated would be shared by all the area's inhabitants.

ONE DESIGN FOR A CENTRAL PHOTOVOLTAIC GENERATING FACILITY

Solar Power in Space

The first significant use of photovoltaics was as a power source for satellites. As was mentioned earlier, the first solar cells for space use were installed in 1958 on Vanguard I. Since then most U.S. satellites and manned missions have employed photovoltaic panels to provide electricity for extended missions. It is widely believed that photovoltaics will continue to be widely used in future space applications.

Space in many ways is an ideal environment for the use of photovoltaics; there is no atmosphere to filter solar radiation, shading is an insignificant problem, and photovoltaic arrays can be placed in an orbit that will provide sunlight 24 hours a day. Unfortunately, these conditions also lead to increased operating temperatures, and premature cell degradation. The long-term use of photovoltaics in space will require the development of mechanisms which will eliminate these problems.

One of the most widely discussed proposals for using photovoltaics in space is the Solar Powered Satellite (SPS). Currently being investigated, this concept envisions a huge photovoltaic array, of several square miles, which is assembled in space. The SPS would generate electricity from the sun, and transmit the collected energy in microwave beams to receiving stations on earth. The satellite would be an ideal use of photovoltaics, since it would generate electricity 24 hours a day. But the feasibility of this proposal is still under discussion, since it would entail multi-billion dollar expenditures and may present potential health hazards to people living close to the receiving stations.

With the advent of the U.S. Space Shuttle and other reuseable space vehicles, many other space missions may be developed which will rely on photovoltaics for power. Currently in the conceptual design

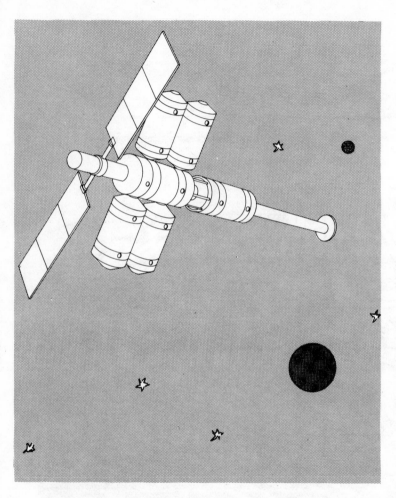

PROPOSED SOLAR AND TERRESTRIAL OBSERVATORY

stage, the Advanced Space Construction Base may be placed in orbit to build satellites, large antennas, and other orbital facilities. Other space facilities could include permanent Space Manufacturing Facilities, which would manufacture products for consumption on earth. The manufacturing process used would take advantage of the vacuum and weightless conditions in space and could include the production of pharmaceuticals, serums, and high-strength magnets. Other concepts under consideration are photovoltaic powered moon bases, orbiting space stations, and a successor to Skylab, the Solar and Terrestrial Observatory. All of these facilities would rely in whole or in part on photovoltaics for electricity. While many of these concepts appear to be overly grandiose, think how realistic a manned mission to the moon, or a space shuttle would have appeared in 1950. The possibilities may be limited only by our imagination.

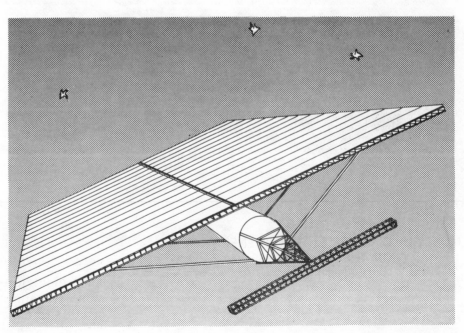

ARTIST'S CONCEPTION OF A 2-MILE
BY 3-MILE SOLAR POWERED SATELLITE

Total Energy Systems

More than 25 percent of the energy produced in the United States is consumed in residential and commercial buildings. An additional 10 percent of primary energy is lost in producing electricity. Consequently, since our homes and businesses consume 35 percent of all the energy we use, photovoltaics will play a large role in meeting these energy needs.

The optimum use of photovoltaics in some cases is in combination with other solar technologies. Such "hybrid" systems will be used with increasing frequency, both as additions to existing homes and businesses ("retrofitting") or as an integral part of new buildings, just as central air conditioning has become a part of home design and construction. The "solar total energy systems" will include photovoltaics for electricity, solar thermal collectors for hot water and heating, storage mediums for heat and coolness storage and temperature control, and passive architectural design to reduce energy consumption.

Buildings currently are constructed for a useful life of 30 years or longer. Most buildings constructed in 1981 will still be in use by 2011 or beyond. By the year 2000, solar electricity and solar heat will have become commonplace and most buildings will have been retrofitted or built to collect solar energy for practical use.

These solar energy systems will have a variety of sizes, capabilities, and features, depending on

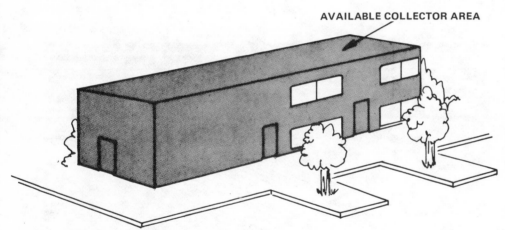

AVAILABLE COLLECTOR AREA

MOST BUILDINGS RECEIVE MORE ENERGY
FROM THE SUN THAN IS
USED INSIDE

the particular use. A photovoltaic array will supply electricity from a roof mounted or field mounted position. This photovoltaic system will probably be connected to the utility, so that electricity will be available when the sun is not shining. The utility connection also will enable the owners of the array to sell back any excess electricity to the utility. The photovoltaic system will include an "electric power distribution panel" which will monitor the electricity produced by the array, and feed excess energy to the utility. The system also may employ an energy storage subsystem.

In addition to electricity, the building will require hot water and heating. Solar thermal collectors, mounted on the roof or near the building will provide hot water or, with a heat pump (a more efficient form of air conditioning and heating), will be used to heat the building. A storage tank filled with water or phase change materials (see Chapter 1) will be used to store excess heat for later use.

In some locations, extreme temperature differences between day and night make it practical to store nighttime coolness to use for daytime cooling. Such storage systems also will use phase change materials to provide air conditioning with little or no electricity cost. The time is near when you will be able to turn on the air conditioner without worrying about the effect it will have on your electric bill.

The description above represents the "active" portion of a hybrid solar system. To fully use the benefits of solar energy, this active system must be combined with passive solar features. In solar homes of the future, these passive solar features will include some of the designs discussed in Chapter 1, such as south-facing windows to heat the house in the winter, and different kinds of shading, either with trees or shades, to block out sun in the warmer months. These buildings also will be well insulated and constructed so

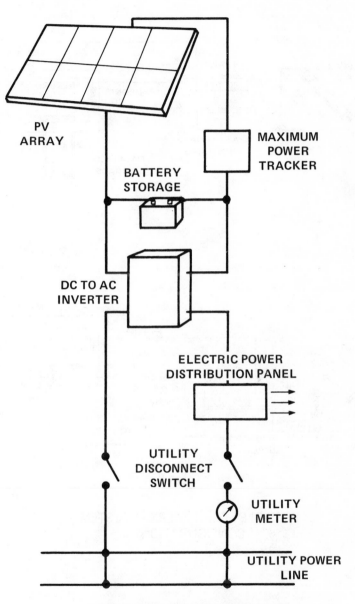

SCHEMATIC PRESENTATION OF
PHOTOVOLTAIC COMPONENT OF
SOLAR TOTAL ENERGY SYSTEM

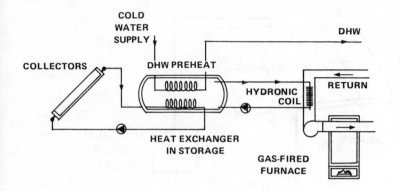

COLD
WATER
SUPPLY

DHW

COLLECTORS

DHW PREHEAT

HYDRONIC
COIL

RETURN

HEAT EXCHANGER
IN STORAGE

GAS-FIRED
FURNACE

RETURN AIR

PUMP

COLLECTORS

HEAT
EXCHANGER

SOLAR
STORAGE
TANK

SUPPLY
AIR

PUMP

COLD WATER
SUPPLY

HOT WATER
DISTRIBUTION

WATER
HEATER

POSSIBLE SOLAR THERMAL SYSTEM
CONFIGURATIONS

that there is a controlled interior environment. Moveable insulation, such as shades and curtains also will be employed to reduce nighttime heat losses through windows and doors.

The combination of these solar and conservation techniques and devices will result in buildings which will meet most of their own energy needs. It will not be long before the millions of barrels of oil which are consumed to heat, cool, and electrify our homes, businesses, and factories will not be required. And our energy needs will be met at a lower overall cost than with the use of fossil fuels or nuclear energy.

It may sound rather optimistic to expect solar total energy systems in widespread use anytime in the near future. But contrary to popular opinion, many passive solar homes, and homes with heat and hot water supplied by solar energy currently are built or being built in locations around the world. It is just one step further to combine the beneficial aspects of passive solar design and active solar systems to have a solar total energy system. MONEGON is a pioneer in developing such a system and currently is designing such a system for a home which is being built in Potomac, Maryland. It will not be long before such systems are commonplace.

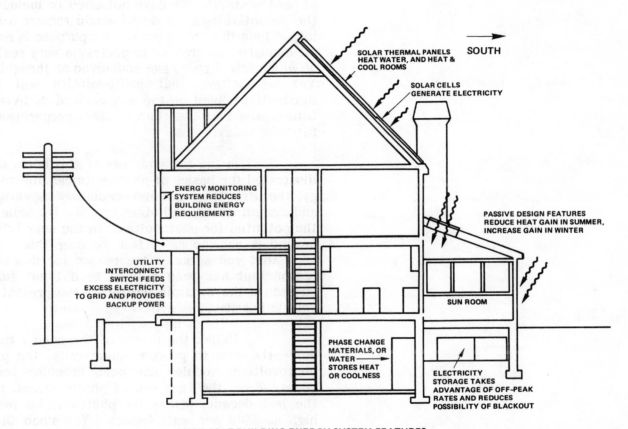

SOUTH

SOLAR THERMAL PANELS
HEAT WATER, AND HEAT &
COOL ROOMS

SOLAR CELLS
GENERATE ELECTRICITY

ENERGY MONITORING
SYSTEM REDUCES
BUILDING ENERGY
REQUIREMENTS

PASSIVE DESIGN FEATURES
REDUCE HEAT GAIN IN SUMMER,
INCREASE GAIN IN WINTER

UTILITY
INTERCONNECT
SWITCH FEEDS
EXCESS ELECTRICITY
TO GRID AND PROVIDES
BACKUP POWER

SUN ROOM

PHASE CHANGE
MATERIALS, OR
WATER
STORES HEAT
OR COOLNESS

ELECTRICITY
STORAGE TAKES
ADVANTAGE OF OFF-PEAK
RATES AND REDUCES
POSSIBILITY OF BLACKOUT

AVAILABLE BUILDING ENERGY SYSTEM FEATURES

POSSIBLE SOLAR TOTAL ENERGY SYSTEM FEATURES

Toward the Solar Future

In the last several pages, we have attempted to describe some of the possible future uses of photovoltaics. We have not tried to include all of the potential uses, to do so would require a chapter longer than this entire book. Our purpose is not to be all-inclusive, but rather to portray a very real future of which few people have conceived or thought likely. Yet we believe that photovoltaics will have a substantial impact on the way each of us lives in the future, and that the time to start preparing for this future is today.

In the ten chapters of this book, we have illustrated the basics of photovoltaics: the technology, the uses, the legal and regulatory aspects, design and system issues, and other topics. We believe that the potential for photovoltaics in the near future and beyond is enormous. After reading this book, we hope that you agree. One reason for this belief, a reason that has been alluded to but not fully discussed, is the dynamic nature of the present photovoltaic industry.

Unlike the prices of the energy resources currently used to produce electricity, the price of photovoltaic modules has been dropping for many years. From the first use of photovoltaics, up until the last decade, prices for photovoltaics ranged as high as $500 per watt (peak). Yet since the early 1970s, the price for photovoltaics has dropped precipitously. In early 1981, photovoltaics could be purchased for almost a hundred times less than the cost a decade earlier. It is anticipated that these prices will drop to about a tenth of present prices in the next few years.

The cause of this decrease of almost 1,000 percent in photovoltaics prices is the dynamic nature of the photovoltaics industry. The industry is a relatively recent addition to the energy field. Prior to the 1970s, only a handful of companies were involved in photovoltaics manufacturing, and these firms produced small quantities of photovoltaics almost exclusively for space applications. It is only since about the time of the oil embargo in 1973-1974 that the industry really began to grow rapidly.

Much has been accomplished in the last six or seven years, as processes and equipment for large-scale production have been developed. The industry has progressed rapidly from its infancy, with new technology improving productivity, increasing solar cell efficiency, and reducing manufacturing costs. Yet the photovoltaics industry currently is much like the automobile industry before Henry Ford introduced new automation techniques. The techniques, processes, and equipment have been developed. In the next few years, these innovations will be further refined in order to mass produce photovoltaic cells.

In the near future, photovoltaics will be manufactured in large automated facilities that will provide inexpensive, high-quality modules for photovoltaic systems to be used for almost any electricity requirement. The production facilities, as with other modern industries, will be highly automated in order to make low-cost reliable products. These plants, which will be virtually pollution-free, will produce photovoltaics at a fraction of their present cost and in much less time than currently required.

For these reasons alone, many energy experts believe that the 1980s will be a period of rapid expansion in the photovoltaics industry. Yet in addition to these developments, the increasing cost of fossil fuels and other nonrenewable energy resources will increase the attractiveness of photovoltaics.

Nonrenewable energy resources are becoming less and less attractive for many reasons. Increasing prices place an intolerable burden on individuals, companies, and our economy in general, both because of the actual cost and because of the additional inflationary effects caused by rapid price increases. The pollution caused by coal, oil, and nuclear energy use has resulted in common occurrences of acid rain, river and ground water contamination, and the uncomfortable possibility of a serious nuclear power plant accident.

The importation of large amounts of oil leaves our economy vulnerable to foreign supply interruptions which actually could threaten our national security and our nation's economic well-being. It is ironic that during the 1973-1974 oil embargo, as we waited for hours in gasoline lines and suffered staggering oil price increases, unlimited quantities of solar energy were at our disposal. It would be truly unfortunate if we allow this valuable and free energy resource to remain under-utilized in the future.

Should we accept our use of coal, nuclear, oil and gas and the detrimental effects this use has on our lives, our environment, and our economy? Or should we supplement these resources with the nonpolluting use of renewable solar conversion technologies such as photovoltaics? In the next few years, photovoltaics will become competitive with non-renewable resources in an almost unlimited number of uses. In fact, several projections have indicated that in the next ten to twelve years, photovoltaics may become the least expensive and most effective means of generating electricity for almost any use in almost any location. Doesn't it make sense to start moving toward this solar future today?

APPENDIX A
Sources Of Information

STATE GOVERNMENT

Where can you find out what your state is doing to conserve energy and promote the use of solar resources? In most states, these programs are handled by several agencies. On the following pages, we have listed states offices and contacts responsible for solar energy and energy conservation programs.*

STATE ENERGY OFFICES, in most states, are responsible for carrying out state energy policies and coordinating programs.

ENERGY EXTENSION SERVICES (EES) are state-level offices, funded and coordinated by the U.S. Department of Energy, and designed to actively promote energy conservation and solar energy at the local level. Families, small businesses, community groups, and local governments are now receiving information and technical assistance through energy extension service programs. (Note: Because the Energy Extension Service program was recently broadened to include all states and U.S. territories, activities in some states may still be under development.)

SOLAR OFFICES, which coordinate solar energy programs, have been created in most states with funding from the Regional Solar Energy Centers. On the following pages, we have listed state solar offices which can provide information to the public.

Some states have created solar policy advisory offices and energy research and development centers. These organizations are referenced on the following pages.

State or Territory	State Energy Offices	Energy Extension Services (EES)	State Solar Offices and Representatives
Alabama	Alabama Energy Management Board 3734 Atlanta Highway Montgomery, Alabama 36130 (205) 832-5010 (800) 572-7226 (State Solar Hotline)	Alabama Energy Extension Service 313 Ross Hall Auburn University Auburn, Alabama 36830 (205) 826-4718 Contact: Dr. John Hoyle, Director	See: Alabama Energy Management Board

*This information was made available through the Solar Energy Information Data Bank of the Solar Energy Research Institute.

Alaska	Alaska State Energy Office Division of Power and Energy MacKay Building, 7th Floor 338 Denali Street Anchorage, Alaska 99501 (907) 272-0527	Alaska Energy Extension Service Division of Power and Energy MacKay Building, 7th Floor 338 Denali Street Anchorage, Alaska 99501 (907) 274-8655 Contact: John Hale, Director	Alaska State Solar Representative Division of Power and Energy MacKay Building, 7th Floor 338 Denali Street Anchorage, Alaska 99501 (907) 276-0508 Contact: Robert E. Shipley
American Samoa		Energy Extension Service Territorial Energy Office Government of American Samoa Pago Pago, American Samoa 96799 Contact: Matt Le'i	
Arizona	Arizona Office of Economic Planning and Development Energy Conservation Office 1700 West Washington, Room 504 Phoenix, Arizona 85007 (602) 255-3303 (800) 352-5499 (State Energy Hotline)	Energy Extension Service Arizona Solar Energy Commission 1700 West Washington, Room 502 Phoenix, Arizona 85007 (602)255-3682 Contact: John Kimball	Arizona State Solar Representative Arizona Solar Energy Commission 1700 West Washington, Suite 502 Phoenix, Arizona 85007 (602) 255-3682 Contact: Donald E. Osborn

| Arkansas | Arkansas State Energy Office Commerce Department 3000 Kavanaugh Little Rock, Arkansas 72205 (501) 371-1379 (800) 482-1122 (State Energy Hotline) | Energy Extension Service Arkansas State Energy Office 3000 Kavanaugh Little Rock, Arkansas 72205 (501) 371-1370 Contact: Paul F. Levy, Director | See: Arkansas State Energy Office |
| California | California Energy Commission 1111 Howe Avenue Sacramento, California 95825 (916) 920-6430 (800) 952-5670 (State Solar Hotline) | California Energy Extension Service Office of Appropriate Technology 1530 Tenth Street Sacramento, California 95814 (916) 445-1803 (916) 322-8901 Contact: Gigi Coe, Public Information Programs Manager | California State Solar Representative 1111 Howe Avenue Sacramento, California 95825 (916) 920-7623 Contact: Larry Levin or Landon Williams California State Solar Representative 6022 West Pico Boulevard Los Angeles, California 90035 (213) 852-5135 Contact: Margaret Gardels, Jan Smutney-Jones, or Alisa Katz |

Colorado	Colorado Office of Energy Conservation 1600 Downing Street, 2nd Floor Denver, Colorado 80218 (303) 839-2507 (800) 234-2105 (State Energy Hotline)	Energy Extension Service Colorado Office of Energy Conservation 1600 Downing Street, 2nd Floor Denver, Colorado 80218 (303) 839-2507 Contact: Robert Brown, Director of Community Programs	Colorado State Solar Representative Colorado Office of Energy Conservation 1600 Downing Street, 2nd Floor Denver, Colorado 80218 (303) 839-2507 (303) 839-2186 Contact: Mark McCray or Dennis Bates
Connecticut	Connecticut Office of Policy and Management Energy Division 80 Washington Street Hartford, Connecticut 06115 (203) 566-3394 (800) 842-1648 (State Energy Hotline)	Connecticut Energy Extension Service Office of Policy and Management 80 Washington Street Hartford, Connecticut 06115 (203) 566-5803 Contact: Bradford S. Chase, Director	Energy Division Connecticut Office of Policy and Management 80 Washington Street Hartford, Connecticut 06115 (203) 566-3394 Contact: Michael Sartori
Delaware	Delaware Energy Office 114 West Water Street P.O. Box 1401 Dover, Delaware 19901 (302) 678-5644 (800) 282-8616 (State Energy Hotline)	Energy Extension Service Delaware Energy Office 114 West Water Street P.O. Box 1401 Dover, Delaware 19901 (302) 678-5644 Contact: Dan Anstine	See: Delaware Energy Office
District of Columbia	District of Columbia Office of Planning and Development 409 District Building 1350 E. Street NW Washington, D.C. 20004 (202) 727-6365	Energy Extension Service 1420 New York Avenue NW 2nd Floor Washington, D.C. 20005 (202) 727-1804 Contact: Jack Warner	See: District of Columbia Office of Planning and Development

Florida	Florida Governor's Energy Office 301 Bryant Building Tallahassee, Florida 32301 (904) 488-6764 (800) 432-0575 (State Solar Hotline)	Energy Extension Service Florida Governor's Energy Office 301 Bryant Building Tallahassee, Florida 32301 (904) 488-6143 Contact: Fernando E. Recio	See: Florida Governor's Energy Office
Georgia	Georgia Office of Energy Resources 270 Washington Street SW Suite 615 Atlanta, Georgia 30334 (404) 656-5176	Energy Extension Service Georgia Office of Energy Resources 270 Washington Street SW Room 615 Atlanta, Georgia 30334 (404) 656-5176 Contact: Elizabeth Robertson	See: Georgia Office of Energy Resources
Guam		Energy Extension Service Guam Energy Office Chase Bank Building, Room 402 P.O. Box 2950 Agana, Guam 96910 447-9845 (via Overseas Operator) Contact: Jesus J. San Agustin, P.E., Administrator	
Hawaii	Hawaii State Energy Office Department of Planning and Economic Development 1164 Bishop Street, Suite 1515 Honolulu, Hawaii 96813 (808) 548-4150	Energy Extension Service Hawaii State Energy Office Department of Planning and Economic Development 1164 Bishop Street, Suite 1515 Honolulu, Hawaii 96813 (808) 548-4080 Contact: Ed Greaney	Hawaii State Solar Representative Center for Science Policy and Technology Assessment P.O. Box 2359 Honolulu, Hawaii 96804 (808) 548-4195 Contact: Dwayne Yoshina

Idaho	Idaho Office of Energy State Capitol Building Boise, Idaho 83720 (208) 334-3800 (800) 632-5954 (State Energy Hotline)	Energy Extension Service Idaho Office of Energy State Capitol Building Boise, Idaho 83720 (208) 334-3800 Contact: Bradley Gore	Idaho State Solar Representative State Capitol Building Boise, Idaho 83720 (208) 334-3800 (208) 342-5435 Contact: Megan Morgan or Nick Cimino
Illinois	Illinois Institute of Natural Resources Divisions of Solar Energy and Conservation 325 West Adams Street Room 300 Springfield, Illinois 62706 (217) 785-2431 (800) 424-9122 (State Energy Hotline)	Energy Extension Service Illinois Institute of Natural Resources 325 West Adams Street Room 300 Springfield, Illinois 62706 (217) 785-2800 Contact: Steve Thomas	Illinois Institute of Natural Resources Alternative Energy Division 325 West Adams Street Room 300 Springfield, Illinois 62706 (217) 785-2431 Contact: Jill Kunka
Indiana	Indiana Energy Office Indiana Department of Commerce 440 North Meridian Street Indianapolis, Indiana 46204 (317) 232-8940	Energy Extension Service Energy Group Indiana Department of Commerce 440 North Meridian Street Indianapolis, Indiana 46204 (317) 232-8940 Contact: Robert Hedding	Energy Group Indiana Department of Commerce 440 North Meridian Street Indianapolis, Indiana 46204 (317) 232-8940 Contact: Clarence L. Warren
Iowa	Iowa Energy Policy Council Lucas Building, 6th Floor Capitol Complex Des Moines, Iowa 50319 (515) 281-4420 (800) 523-1114 (State Energy Hotline)	Iowa Energy Extension Service 110 Marston Hall Iowa State University Ames, Iowa 50011 (515) 294-4266 Contact: K. Baker, Director	Iowa Energy Policy Council Capitol Complex Des Moines, Iowa 50319 (515) 281-8071 Contact: Philip Svanoe

Kansas	Kansas Energy Office 214 West 6th Street Topeka, Kansas 66603 (913) 296-2496 (800) 432-3537 (State Energy Hotline)	Kansas Energy Extension Service 214 West 6th Street Topeka, Kansas 66603 (913) 296-2496 Contact: David Martin	Kansas Energy Office 214 West 6th Street Topeka, Kansas 66603 (913) 296-2496 Contact: David Martin
Kentucky	Kentucky Department of Energy Capitol Plaza Tower Frankfort, Kentucky 40601 (502) 564-7416 (800) 372-2978 (State Energy Hotline)	Kentucky Energy Extension Service P.O. Box 11888 Ironworks Pike Lexington, Kentucky 40578 Contact: John Stapleton	See: Kentucky Department of Energy
Louisiana	Louisiana Division of Natural Resources Department of Research and Development P.O. Box 44156 Baton Rouge, Louisiana 70804 (504) 342-4592	Energy Extension Service Louisiana State University Cooperative Extension Service Knapp Hall Baton Rouge, Louisiana 70803 (504) 342-4500	See: Louisiana Division of Natural Resources, Department of Research and Development
Maine	Maine Office of Energy Resources 55 Capitol Street Augusta, Maine 04330 (207) 289-3811	Energy Extension Service Maine Office of Energy Resources 55 Capitol Street Augusta, Maine 04333 (207) 289-3811 Contact: Kathy Murray, Director	Maine Office of Energy Resources 55 Capitol Street Augusta, Maine 04330 (207) 289-3811 Contact: Richard McGinley

Maryland	Maryland Energy Policy Office 301 West Preston Street Suite 1302 Baltimore, Maryland 21201 (301) 383-6810 (800) 492-5903 (State Energy Hotline)	Energy Extension Service Maryland Energy Policy Office 301 West Preston Street Suite 1302 Baltimore, Maryland 21201 (301) 383-6810 Contact: Jill Lion	See: Maryland Energy Policy Office
Massachusetts	Massachusetts Office of Energy Resources 73 Tremont Street, Room 700 Boston, Massachusetts 02108 (617) 727-4732 (800) 922-8265 ("Energyphone")	Energy Extension Service Massachusetts Office of Energy Resources 73 Tremont Street Boston, Massachusetts 02108 (617) 727-5064 Contact: Ines Feller	Massachusetts Office of Energy Resources 73 Tremont Street Room 840 Boston, Massachusetts 02108 (617) 727-7297 Contact: Buz Laughlin
Michigan	Michigan Energy Administration P.O. Box 30228 Lansing, Michigan 48909 (517) 373-6430 (800) 292-4704 (State Energy Hotline)	Michigan Energy Extension Service 6520 Mercantile Way Suite 1 Lansing, Michigan 48910 (517) 373-0480 Contact: Dennis Sykes, Director	Michigan Energy Administration P.O. Box 30228 Lansing, Michigan 48909 (517) 373-6430 Contact: Thomas G. Heck
Minnesota	Minnesota Energy Agency 980 American Center Building 150 East Kellogg Boulevard St. Paul, Minnesota 55101 (612) 296-5120 (800) 652-9747 (State Energy Hotline)	Energy Extension Service Minnesota Energy Agency 980 American Center Building 150 East Kellogg Boulevard St. Paul, Minnesota 55101 (612) 296-8898 Contact: Karen Martin	Minnesota Energy Agency 980 American Center Building 150 East Kellogg Boulevard St. Paul, Minnesota 55101 (612) 296-4737 Contact: John Dunlop

Mississippi	Mississippi Office of Energy 455 North Lamar, Suite 228 Jackson, Mississippi 39201 (601) 981-5099	Mississippi Energy Extension Center Mississippi State University P.O. Box 5406 Mississippi State, Mississippi 39762 (601) 325-3136 Contact: Dr. William L. Linder, Coordinator	See: Mississippi Office of Energy
Missouri	Missouri Division of Energy P.O. Box 176 Jefferson City, Missouri 65102 (314) 751-4000 (800) 392-0717 (State Energy Hotline)	Energy Extension Service Missouri Division of Energy P.O. Box 176 Jefferson City, Missouri 65102 (314) 751-4000 Contact: Gary Cullen	Missouri Division of Energy P.O. Box 176 Jefferson City, Missouri 65102 (314) 751-4000 Contact: Herbert Wade
Montana	Montana Department of Natural Resources and Conservation Energy Division 32 South Ewing Street Helena, Montana 59601 (406) 449-3940	Energy Extension Service Montana Department of Natural Resources and Conservation Energy Division 32 South Ewing Street Helena, Montana 59601 (406) 449-3780 Contact: Paul Cartwright	Montana State Solar Representative Montana Department of Natural Resources and Conservation Energy Division 32 South Ewing Street Helena, Montana 59601 (406) 449-3940 Contact: J. Lee Cook
Nebraska	Nebraska Energy Office 301 Centennial Mall Lincoln, Nebraska 68509 (402) 471-2867	Energy Extension Service W-181 Nebraska Hall University of Nebraska Lincoln, Nebraska 68588 (402) 472-3181 Contact: Dr. Lagerstrom, Director	University of Nebraska W-191 Nebraska Hall Lincoln, Nebraska 68588 (402) 472-3414 Contact: Robert Youngberg

Nevada	Nevada Department of Energy 1050 East William, Suite 405 Carson City, Nevada 89701 (702) 885-5157	Energy Extension Service Nevada Department of Energy 400 West King Carson City, Nevada 89710 (702) 885-5157 Contact: Noel A. Clark, Director	Nevada State Solar Representative Energy Conservation and Planning Department of Energy 1050 East William, Suite 405 Carson City, Nevada 89701 (702) 885-5157 Contact: Robert Loux Nevada State Solar Representative Desert Research Institute 1500 Buchanan Boulevard Boulder City, Nevada 89005 (702) 293-4217 Contact: Chuck Miller
New Hampshire	New Hampshire Governor's Council on Energy 2 1/2 Beacon Street Concord, New Hampshire 03301 (603) 271-2711 (800) 852-3466 (State Energy Hotline)	Energy Extension Service New Hampshire Governor's Council on Energy 2 1/2 Beacon Street Concord, New Hampshire 03301 (603) 271-2711 Contact: Janet Harris	New Hampshire Governor's Council on Energy 2 1/2 Beacon Street Concord, New Hampshire 03301 (603) 271-2711 Contact: Julie Eades
New Jersey	New Jersey Department of Energy Office of Alternate Technology 101 Commerce Street Newark, New Jersey 07102 (201) 648-6293 (800) 492-4242 (State Energy Hotline)	Energy Extension Service New Jersey Department of Energy 101 Commerce Street Newark, New Jersey 07102 (201) 648-3900 Contact: Sue Waldman	Office of Alternate Technology New Jersey Department of Energy 101 Commerce Street Newark, New Jersey 07102 (201) 648-6293 Contact: William Groth

New Mexico	New Mexico Energy and Minerals Department P.O. Box 2770 Santa Fe, New Mexico 87503 (505) 827-2472 (800) 432-6782 (State Energy Hotline)	New Mexico Energy Extension Service P.O. Box 00 Santa Fe, New Mexico 87501 (505) 827-2386 Contact: Dal Symes	New Mexico State Solar Representative Energy Conservation and Management Div. P.O. Box 2770 Santa Fe, New Mexico 87501 (505) 827-5621 Contact: John W. Goeller
New York	New York State Energy Office Agency Building 2, 8th Floor Empire State Plaza Albany, New York 12223 (518) 474-7016 (800) 342-3722 (State Energy Hotline)	Energy Extension Service New York State Energy Office 2 Rockefeller Plaza Albany, New York 12223 (518) 474-4083 Contact: Sandy Schuman, Coordinator	New York State Energy Office Agency Building 2, 8th Floor Albany, New York 12223 (518) 474-7016 (518) 473-8667 Contact: Monica McGuire
North Carolina	North Carolina Department of Commerce Energy Division Dobbs Building Raleigh, North Carolina 27611 (919) 733-2230 (800) 662-7131 (State Energy Hotline)	Energy Extension Service North Carolina Department of Commerce Energy Division Dobbs Building Raleigh, North Carolina 27611 (919) 733-2230 Contact: John Manuel	See: North Carolina Department of Commerce, Energy Division
North Dakota	North Dakota Energy Office 1533 North 12th Street Bismarck, North Dakota 58501 (701) 224-2250	Energy Extension Service North Dakota Office of Energy Management and Coordination 1533 North 12th Street Bismarck, North Dakota 58501 (701) 224-2250 Contact: Bruce Westerberg	North Dakota Energy Office 1533 North 12th Street Bismarck, North Dakota 58501 (701) 224-2250 Contact: John Conrad

Northern Mariana Islands		Energy Project Coordinator Office of the Governor Commonwealth of the Northern Mariana Islands P.O. Box 1115 Saipan, Mariana Islands CM-96950 7174 or 6114 (via overseas operator) Contact: George Chan, Coordinator	
Ohio	Ohio Department of Energy 30 East Broad Street 34th Floor Columbus, Ohio 43215 (614) 466-6797 (800) 282-9234 (State Energy Hotline)	Energy Extension Service Ohio Department of Energy 30 East Broad Street 34th Floor Columbus, Ohio 43215 (614) 466-6747 Contact: Thomas P. Ryan, Deputy Director	Ohio Department of Energy 30 East Broad Street 34th Floor Columbus, Ohio 43215 (614) 466-8277 Contact: Dr. Leon E. Winget
Oklahoma	Oklahoma Department of Energy 4400 North Lincoln Boulevard Suite 251 Oklahoma City, Oklahoma 73105 (405) 521-3441	Energy Extension Service Oklahoma Department of Energy 4400 North Lincoln Boulevard, Suite 251 Oklahoma City, Oklahoma 73105 (405) 521-2995 (405) 521-3941 Contact: Patty Barrett	See: Oklahoma Department of Energy

Oregon	Oregon Department of Energy Labor and Industries Building Salem, Oregon 97310 (503) 378-4128 (800) 452-7813 ("Access 800" State Govt. Hotline)	Energy Extension Service 114 Dearborn Hall Oregon State University Corvallis, Oregon 97331 (503) 754-3004 Contact: Owen D. Osborne, Coordinator	Oregon State Solar Representative Oregon Department of Energy Labor and Industries Building Salem, Oregon 97310 Contact: John Kaufman
Pennsylvania	Pennsylvania Governor's Energy Council 1625 North Front Street Harrisburg, Pennsylvania 17102 (717) 783-8610 (800) 882-8400 (State Energy Conservation Hotline)	Energy Extension Service Pennsylvania Governor's Energy Council 1625 North Front Street Harrisburg, Pennsylvania 17102 (717) 783-8610 Contact: John Hafer	Pennsylvania Governor's Energy Council 1625 North Front Street Harrisburg, Pennsylvania 17102 (717) 783-8610 Contact: Lucy Lott
Puerto Rico	Puerto Rico Office of Energy Minillas Governmental Center North Building Office, Postal Stop 22 P.O. Box 41089 Minillas Station Santurce, Puerto Rico 00940 (809) 726-3636	Energy Extension Service Puerto Rico Office of Energy Minillas Governmental Center North Building Office, Postal Stop 22 P.O. Box 41089 Minillas Station Santurce, Puerto Rico 00940 (809) 726-0196 (809) 726-5055 Contact: Patricia Burmudez, Director	See: Puerto Rico Office of Energy

Rhode Island	Rhode Island Governor's Energy Office 80 Dean Street Providence, Rhode Island 02903 (401) 277-3773 (will accept collect calls from state residents)	Energy Extension Service Rhode Island Governor's Energy Office 80 Dean Street Providence, Rhode Island 02903 (401) 277-3370 Contact: Vincent Graziano, Coordinator	Energy Capability and Management Rhode Island Governor's Energy Office 80 Dean Street Providence, Rhode Island 02903 (401 277-3374 (401) 277-3774 Contact: Shelly Greenfiled
South Carolina	South Carolina Department of Energy Resources 1122 Lady Street, Suite 1120 Columbia, South Carolina 29201	Energy Extension Service Project South Carolina State Board for Technical and Comprehensive Education 1429 Senate Street Columbia, South Carolina 29201 (803) 758-5794 Contact: Earle W. Moore, Director	See: South Carolina Department of Energy Resources
South Dakota	South Dakota Office of Energy Policy Capital Lake Plaza Pierre, South Dakota 57501 (605) 773-3604 (800) 592-1865 ("Tie Line" State Govt. Hotline)	Energy Extension Service South Dakota Office of Energy Policy Capital Lake Plaza Pierre, South Dakota 57501 (605) 773-3603 Contact: Shelley Stingley	South Dakota State Energy Office Capital Lake Plaza Pierre, South Dakota 57501 (607) 773-3603 Contact: Verne Brakie

Tennessee	Tennessee Energy Office 226 Capital Boulevard, Suite 707 Nashville, Tennessee 37219 (615) 741-2994 (800) 342-1340 (State Energy Hotline)	Tennessee Energy Extension Service 226 Capitol Boulevard, Suite 615 Nashville, Tennessee 37219 (615) 741-6677 Contact: Douglas Bennett Jr., Director	See: Tennessee Energy Office
Texas	Texas Energy and Natural Resources Advisory Council 411 West 13th Street Austin, Texas 78701 (512) 475-5588	Energy Extension Service Texas Energy and Natural Resources Advisory Council Executive Building 411 West 13th Street Suite 804 Austin, Texas 78701 (512) 475-5407 Contact: Chris Roitsch	See: Texas Energy and Natural Resources Advisory Council
Utah	Utah Energy Office Empire Building, Suite 101 231 East 400 South Salt Lake City, Utah 84111 (801) 533-5424 (800) 662-3633 (State Energy Hotline)	Energy Extension Service Utah Energy Office Empire Building, Suite 101 231 East 400 South Salt Lake City, Utah 84111 (801) 533-5424 Contact: Jim Byrne	Utah State Solar Representative Utah Energy Office Empire Building, Suite 101 231 East 400 South Salt Lake City, Utah 84111 (801) 533-5424 Contact: Kerry L. Faigle or Joan Degiorgio
Vermont	Vermont Energy Office State Office Building Montpelier, Vermont 05602 (802) 828-2393 (800) 642-3281 (State Energy Hotline)	Energy Extension Service State Office Building Montpelier, Vermont 05602 (802) 828-2393 Contact: Bruce Haskell, Deputy Director	Vermont State Energy State Office Building Montpelier, Vermont 05602 (802) 828-2393 Contact: David Pinkham

Virginia	Virginia State Office of Emergency and Energy Services Energy Division 310 Turner Road Richmond, Virginia 23225 (804) 745-3245 (800) 552-3831 (State Energy Hotline)	Energy Extension Service Virginia State Office of Emergency and Energy Services Energy Division 310 Turner Road Richmond, Virginia 23225 (804) 745-3245 Contact: Temple Bayliss, Director	See: Virginia State Office of Emergency and Energy Services, Energy Division
Virgin Islands	Virgin Islands Energy Office P.O. Box 90 St. Thomas, Virgin Islands 00801 (809) 774-0750	Energy Study College of the Virgin Islands St. Thomas, U.S. Virgin Islands 00801 (809) 774-1251 ext. 249 Contact: Michael J. Canoy, Director	See: Virgin Islands Energy Office
Washington	Washington State Energy Office 400 East Union, 1st Floor Olympia, Washington 98504 (206) 753-2417	Washington Energy Extension Service Cooperative Extension Service, AG-Phase II Washington State University Pullman, Washington 99164 (509) 335-2511 Contact: J. Orville Young, Director	Washington State Solar Representative SMT – F515 University of Washington Seattle, Washington 98122 (206) 543-1249 Contact: Jay Luboff or Evan Brown Washington State Solar Representative P.O. Box 295 Winthrop, Washington 98862 (509) 996-2451 Contact: Aileen Jeffries

West Virginia	West Virginia Fuel and Energy Office 1262 1/2 Greenbriar Street Charleston, West Virginia 25311 (304) 348-8860 (800) 642-9012 (State Energy Hotline)	Energy Extension Service West Virginia Fuel and Energy Office 1262 1/2 Greenbriar Street Charleston, West Virginia 25311 (304) 348-8860 Contact: Ron Potesta	See: West Virginia Fuel and Energy Office
Wisconsin	Wisconsin Office of State Planning and Energy One West Wilson Street Room 201 Madison, Wisconsin 53702 (608) 266-8234	Wisconsin Energy Extension Service University of Wisconsin Extension 432 North Lake Street Room 435 Madison, Wisconsin 53706 (608) 263-1662 (608) 263-7950 Contact: William Bernhagen, Director	Wisconsin Solar Energy Office One West Wilson Street Room 201 Madison, Wisconsin 53702 (608) 266-9861 Contact: Bonnie Albright
Wyoming	Wyoming Energy Conservation Office 320 West 25th Street Cheyenne, Wyoming 82002 (307) 777-7131 (800) 442-8334 (State Solar Referral Hotline) (800) 442-2744 (State Govt. Hotline)	Wyoming Energy Extension Service University Station Box 3295 Laramie, Wyoming 82071 (307) 766-3362 (800) 442-6783 (State Energy Extension Service Hotline) Contact: Ronald White, Program Administrator	Wyoming State Solar Representative Rocky Mountain Institute of Energy and Environment P.O. Box 3965 Laramie, Wyoming 82071 (307) 766-6760 Contact: Florence Baker

WESTERN SOLAR UTILIZATION NETWORK
(WESTERN SUN)

Pioneer Park Building
715 SW Morrison
Portland, Oregon 97204
(503) 241-1222

NATIONAL SOLAR HEATING AND COOLING
INFORMATION CENTER (NSHCIC)

P.O. Box 1607
Rockville, Maryland 20850
(800) 523-2929 (Continental U.S. outside
Pennsylvania)
(800) 462-4983 (Pennsylvania only)
(800) 523-4700 (Alaska and Hawaii only)

MID-AMERICA SOLAR ENERGY COMPLEX
(MASEC)

8140 26th Avenue South
Bloomington, Minnesota 55420
(612) 853-0400

SOLAR ENERGY RESEARCH INSTITUTE
(SERI)

1617 Cole Boulevard
Golden, Colorado 80401
(303) 231-1415
(800) 525-5555 (alcohol fuel inquiries from
the U.S. outside Colorado)
(800) 332-8339 (alcohol fuel inquiries from
Colorado outside Denver)
(303) 231-7303 (alcohol fuel inquiries from
Denver only)

SOUTHERN SOLAR ENERGY CENTER
(SSEC)

61 Perimeter Park
Atlanta, Georgia 30341
(404) 458-8765

NORTHEAST SOLAR ENERGY CENTER
(NESEC)

470 Atlantic Avenue
Boston, Massachusetts 02110
(617) 292-9250

ARIZONA STATE UNIVERSITY LIBRARY

Solar Energy Collection
Tempe, Arizona 85281
(602) 965-7608

CALIFORNIA OFFICE OF APPROPRIATE
TECHNOLOGY

1530 Tenth Street
Sacramento, California 95814

COLORADO ENERGY RESEARCH INSTITUTE

2221 East Street
Golden, Colorado 80401
(303) 279-2881

ENERGY RESOURCES CENTER

U.S. Department of Energy
111 Pine Street
San Francisco, California 94111
(415) 556-7328

CENTER FOR ENERGY POLICY AND RESEARCH
NEW YORK INSTITUTE OF TECHNOLOGY
(NYIT)

Old Westbury
New York 11568
(516) 686-7578

CENTER FOR SOLAR ENERGY APPLICATIONS

San Jose State University
Washington Square
San Jose, California 95192
(408) 277-2939

FLORIDA SOLAR ENERGY CENTER

300 State Road 401
Cape Canaveral, Florida 32920
(305) 783-0300
(800) 432-0575 (State Solar Hotline)

HAWAII NATURAL ENERGY INSTITUTE
(HNEI)

2540 Dole Street
Honolulu, Hawaii 96822
(808) 948-8890

INSTITUTE OF ENERGY CONVERSION

Energy Information Services
University of Delaware
1 Pike Creek Center
Wilmington, Delaware 19808
(302) 994-0915
(302) 995-7155

JOHNSON ENVIRONMENTAL AND ENERGY
CENTER, UNIVERSITY OF ALABAMA

P.O. Box 1247
Huntsville, Alabama 35807
(205) 895-6257
(800) 572-7226 (Alabama only)

NASA LEWIS RESEARCH CENTER
TECHNOLOGY UTILIZATION OFFICE

21000 Brook Park Road
Cleveland, Ohio 44135
(216) 433-4000 ext. 6833

NASA MARSHALL SPACE FLIGHT CENTER
TECHNOLOGY UTILIZATION OFFICE

Code AT01
Marshall Space Flight Center, Alabama 35812

MASSACHUSETTS SOLAR ACTION OFFICE

73 Tremont Street, Room 800
Boston, Massachusetts 02108
(617) 727-7297

NASA LANGLEY RESEARCH CENTER
TECHNOLOGY UTILIZATION OFFICE

Hampton, Virginia 23665

NEW MEXICO ENERGY INSTITUTE
AT NEW MEXICO STATE UNIVERSITY

P.O. Box 3 E.
Las Cruces, New Mexico 88003
(505) 646-1745

NEW MEXICO ENERGY INSTITUTE
AT UNIVERSITY OF NEW MEXICO

117 Richmond Drive NE
Albuquerque, New Mexico 87106

NEW MEXICO SOLAR ENERGY INSTITUTE

.

Box 3 SOL
Las Cruces, New Mexico 88003
(505) 656-1846

PACIFIC NORTHWEST LABORATORIES

Wind Energy Program
P.O. Box 999, Building HS-1
Richland, Washington 99352

SOLAR ENERGY APPLICATIONS
COLORADO STATE UNIVERSITY

Fort Collins, Colorado 80523
(303) 491-8618

SOLAR ENERGY CENTER
DEPARTMENT OF MECHANICAL ENGR.
UNIVERSITY OF FLORIDA

Gainesville, Florida 32611

PALO ALTO RESOURCE CONSERVATION PROGRAM

250 Hamilton Avenue
Palo Alto, California 94301
(415) 329-2241

REGIONAL ENERGY/ENVIRONMENT
INFORMATION CENTER

Denver Public Library
1357 Broadway
Denver, Colorado 80203
(303) 837-5994 (will accept collect calls from states within service area)

SOUTHERN ENERGY/ENVIRONMENTAL
INFORMATION CENTER

One Exchange Place
2300 Peachford Road, Suite 1230
Atlanta, Georgia 30338
(404) 455-8841

TECHNOLOGY APPLICATIONS CENTER
INST. OF APPLIED RESEARCH SERVICES
UNIVERSITY OF NEW MEXICO

Albuquerque, New Mexico 87131
(505) 277-3622

SOLAR ENERGY CENTER
DEPARTMENT OF ARCHITECTURE
UNIVERSITY OF OREGON

Eugene, Oregon 97403

SANDIA LABORATORIES

Advanced Energy Projects
Division 4715
Albuquerque, New Mexico 87185

SMITHSONIAN SCIENCE INFORMATION
EXCHANGE, INC. (SSIE)

170 M Street NW, Room 300
Washington, D.C. 20036
(202) 381-4211

TENNESSEE VALLEY AUTHORITY (TVA)

Information Office
400 Commerce Avenue
Knoxville, Tennessee 37902
(800) 251-9242 (TVA service area outside
Tennessee)
(800) 362-9250 (Tennessee only)

ROCKY FLATS PLANT

Wind Energy Program
Rockwell International Energy
Systems Group
P.O. Box 464
Golden, Colorado 80401

SOLARCAL

1111 Howe Avenue, Suite 315
Sacramento, California 95825
(916) 920-7921
(800) 952-5670 (State Solar Hotline)

SOLAR DATA CENTER
TRINITY UNIVERSITY

Box 500
715 Stadium Drive
San Antonio, Texas 78284

UNIVERSITY OF WISCONSIN SOLAR
ENERGY LABORATORY

Engineering Research Building
1500 Johnson Drive
Madison, Wisconsin 53706
(608) 263-1586

UNDERGROUND SPACE CENTER
UNIVERSITY OF MINNESOTA

11 Mines and Metallurgy
221 Church Street SE
Minneapolis, Minnesota 55455

WESTERN REGIONAL INFORMATION
SERVICE CENTER (WRISC)

Lawrence Berkeley laboratory
Building 50, Room 130
Berkeley, California 94720
(415) 486-6307

Additional Information:

Listed below are individuals and organizations which can help provide more information on solar energy.

American Institute of Architects, 1735 New York Ave., N.W., Washington, D. C. 20006, 785-7300.

Friends of the Earth, 620 C St., S.E., Washington, D.C. 20003, 543-4312.

Environmental Action Reprint Service, Box 545, La Veta, Colo., 81005, 303-742-3221.

Citizen's Energy Project, 783-0452.

Institute for Local Self-Reliance, 1717 18th St., N.W., Washington, D.C. 20009.

Environmental Action, 1346 Conn. Ave., N.W., Washington, D.C. 20036, 833-1845.

Sierra Club, 330 Penn. Ave., S.E., Washington, D.C. 20003, 547-1144.

Environmental Policy Center, 317 Penn. Ave., S.E., Washington, D. C. 2003, 547-6500.

American Wind Energy Association, 1621 Conn. Ave., N.W., Washington, D.C. 20009, 667-9137.

DOE Regional Offices:

The Department of Energy operates regional offices which can provide citizens with information on solar, conservation and other energy issues. They are listed below:

Region I: Harold Keohane, Analex Building, Room 700, 150 Causeway St., Boston, Mass., 02114. 617-223-3701. Covers Connecticut, Maine, New Hampshire, Massachusetts, Rhode Island, Vermont.

Region II: Robert Low, 26 Federal Plaza, Room 3206, New York, N.Y., 10007. 212-264-1021. New York, New Jersey, Puerto Rico, Virgin Islands.

Region III: Bernard Snyder, 1421 Cherry St., 10th Floor, Philadelphia, Pa., 10102. 215-597-3890. Delaware, Maryland, Pennsylvania, Virginia, West Virginia, District of Columbia.

Region IV: Roy Pettit, 1655 Peachtree St., N.E., 8th Floor, Atlanta, Ga., 30309. 404-881-2838. Alabama, Florida, Georgia, Kentucky, Mississippi, North Carolina, South Carolina, Tennessee.

Region V: Robert Bauer, 175 West Jackson Blvd., Room A-333, Chicago, Ill., 60604. 312-353-0540. Illinois, Indiana, Minnesota, Michigan, Wisconsin, Ohio.

Region VI: Curtis Carlson, Jr., P.O. Box 35228, 2626 W. Mockingbird Lane, Dallas, Tex., 75235. 214-749-7345. Arkansas, Louisiana, New Mexico, Oklahoma, Texas.

Region VII: Mary O'Halloran, 324 East 11th St., Kansas City, Mo., 64106. 816-374-816-374-2061. Iowa, Kansas, Missouri, Nebraska.

Region VIII: Charles Metzger, P.O. Box 26247 Belmar Branch, 1075 South Yukon St., Lakewood, Colo., 80226. 303-234-2420. Colorado, Montana, North Dakota, South Dakota, Utah, Wyoming.

Region IX: William Arntz, 111 Pine St., Third Floor, San Francisco, Calif., 94111. 415-566-7216. Arizona, California, Hawaii, Guam, American Samoa, Nevada.

Region X: Jack Robertson, 1992 Federal Building, 915 Second Ave., Seattle, Wash. 98174. 206-442-7280. Alaska, Idaho, Oregon, Washington.

APPENDIX B
Conversion Factors

CONVERSION FACTORS

Multiply:	By:	To Obtain:
Energy		
British Thermal Units	1,055.056	Joules
British Thermal Units	0.0002931	Kilowatt-hours
British Thermal Units	778.17	Foot-pounds force
British Thermal Units	252.04	Calories
Joules	0.0009478	British Thermal Units
Kilowatt-hours	3412.14	British Thermal Units
Foot-pounds force	0.001285	British Thermal Units
Calories	0.003968	British Thermal Units
Kilocalories	1,000	Calories
Watt-hours	0.001	Kilowatt-hours
Watt-second	1	Joules
Kilowatt-hours	3,600,000	Joules
Calories	4.186	Joules
Quad	10^{15}	British Thermal Units
Barrel, oil (crude)	5,800,000	British Thermal Units
Therms	100,000	British Thermal Units
Langleys-centimeter^2	1	Calories

CONVERSION FACTORS (continued)

Multiply:	By:	To Obtain:
Power		
Watt	3.413	British Thermal Units/hour
Watt	0.001341	Horsepower
Watt	0.7376	Foot-pounds force/second
British Thermal Units/hour	0.293	Watt
Horsepower	745.7	Watt
Foot-pounds force/second	1.3558	Watt
Kilowatt	1,000	Watt
Foot-pounds force/second	0.001818	Horsepower
Horsepower	2545.1	British Thermal Units/hour
Metric Horsepower	0.9862	Horsepower
Tons of Refrigeration	3,516	Watts
Area		
Square meters	1.19599	Square yards
Square meters	1550.003	Square inches
Square meters	10.7639	Square feet
Acres	43,560	Square feet
Acres	0.001562	Square miles
Hectares	2.4710	Acres
Square feet	0.0929	Square meters
Square kilometers	0.3861	Square miles
Square miles	2.5900	Square kilometers
Square yards	0.8361	Square meters

CONVERSION FACTORS (continued)

Multiply:	By:	To Obtain:
Length		
Feet	30.48	Centimeters
Inches	2.54	Centimeters
Meters	39.37	Inches
Meters	3.2808	Feet
Meters	1.09	Yards
Kilometers	.62	Miles
Feet	0.3048	Meters
Yards	0.9144	Meters
Miles	5,280	Feet
Miles	1.6093	Kilometers
Microns	1×10^{-4}	Centimeters
Weight		
Tons (short)	2,000	Pounds
Tons (short)	0.907185	Metric tons
Metric tons	2,204.62	Pounds
Grams	0.0353	Ounces
Grams	0.002205	Pounds
Kilograms	2.2046	Pounds
Ounces	28.3495	Grams
Pounds	0.4536	Kilograms

CONVERSION FACTORS (Continued)

Multiply:	By:	To Obtain:
Volume		
Cubic meter	35.32	Cubic feet
Cubic meter	1.3079	Cubic yards
Cubic feet	.0283	Cubic meters
Cubic yards	.7646	Cubic meters
Acre-feet	1,233.5	Cubic meters
Gallons	3.7853	Liters
Gallons	0.003785	Cubic meters
Gallons	0.13368	Cubic feet
Liters	0.001	Cubic meters
Liters	0.0353	Cubic feet

CONVERSION FACTORS (Continued)

<u>Temperatures</u>

To convert Degrees Fahrenheit ($^{\circ}$F) to Degrees Celsius ($^{\circ}$C) the following formula can be used:

$$^{\circ}C = \frac{^{\circ}F - 32}{1.8}$$

To convert Degrees Celsius ($^{\circ}$C) to Degrees Fahrenheit ($^{\circ}$F) the following formula can be used:

$$^{\circ}F = (^{\circ}C \times 1.8) + 32$$

APPENDIX C
Insolation Data

APPENDIX C
INSOLATION DATA

      The following figures show the available solar energy throughout the world at the solstices and equinoxes. More detailed figures are also presented for the United States. The lines running through the figures represent those locations with equivalent solar energy availability. The numbers labeling the lines refer to the kilowatt hours of solar energy falling on one square meter of ground or horizontal surface in a day. This data represents average conditions for a day at that time of year but does not tell anything about a particular day. The reader is referred to Chapter 2 which discusses sunlight and the solar energy in more detail.

Conversion Table for Tables C-2 through C-5

cal/cm^2		kWh/m^2
50	=	.6
100	=	1.2
130	=	1.7
200	=	2.3
250	=	2.9
300	=	3.5
350	=	4.1
400	=	4.6
430	=	5/2
500	=	5.8
550	=	6.4
600	=	7.0
650	=	7.6
700	=	8.1
750	=	8.7
$\dfrac{cal}{cm^2}$		$\dfrac{kWh}{m^2\text{-day}}$

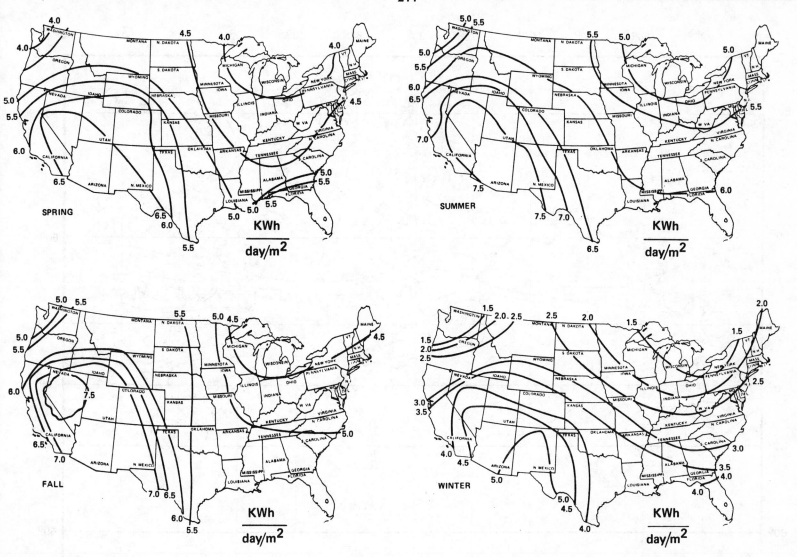

SEASONAL INSOLATION DATA FOR THE UNITED STATES

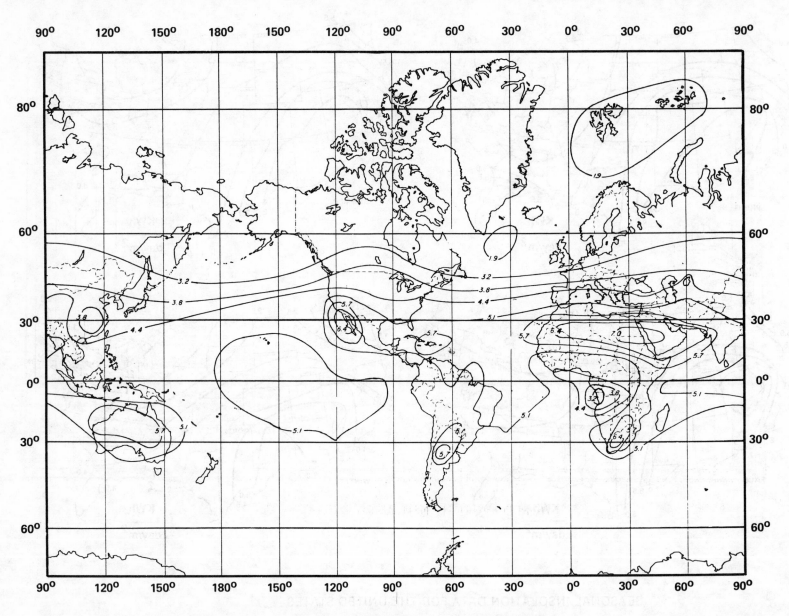

WORLD ANNUAL AVERAGE INSOLATION DATA (KWh/DAY/M²)

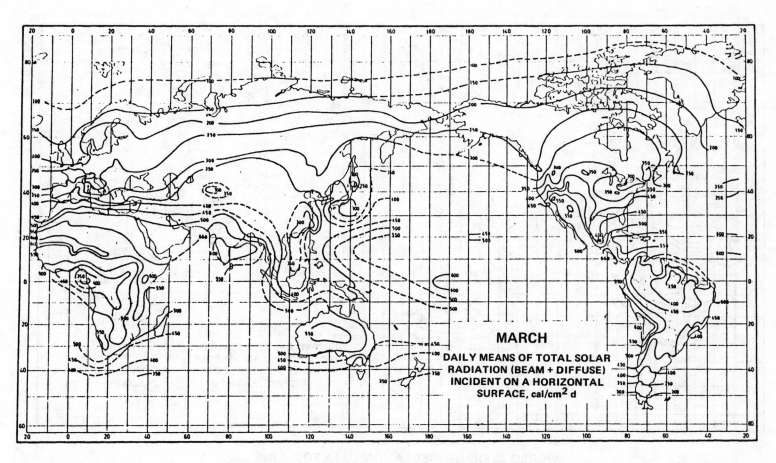

MARCH

DAILY MEANS OF TOTAL SOLAR
RADIATION (BEAM + DIFFUSE)
INCIDENT ON A HORIZONTAL
SURFACE, cal/cm^2 d

WORLD AVERAGE INSOLATION DATA FOR MARCH

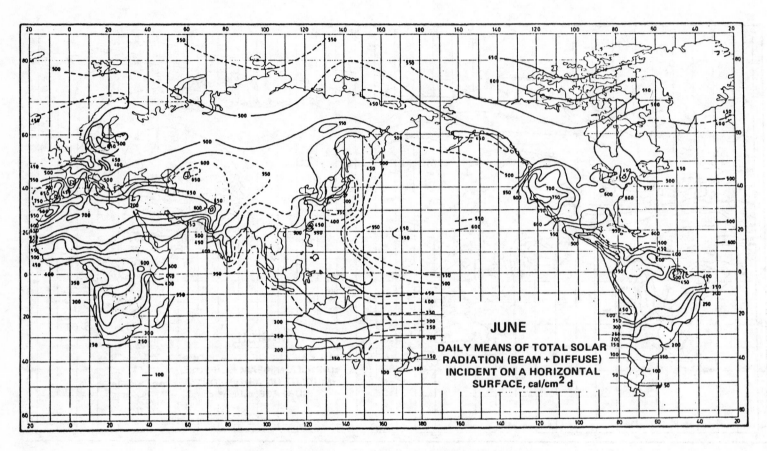

WORLD AVERAGE INSOLATION DATA FOR JUNE

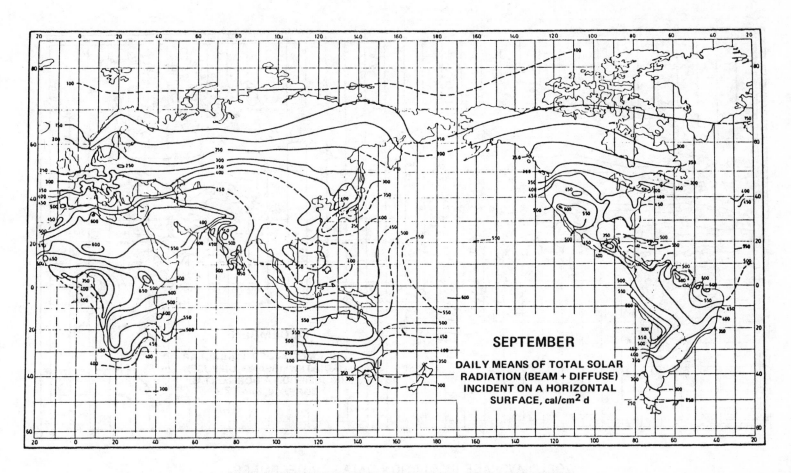

SEPTEMBER

DAILY MEANS OF TOTAL SOLAR
RADIATION (BEAM + DIFFUSE)
INCIDENT ON A HORIZONTAL
SURFACE, cal/cm^2 d

WORLD AVERAGE INSOLATION DATA FOR SEPTEMBER

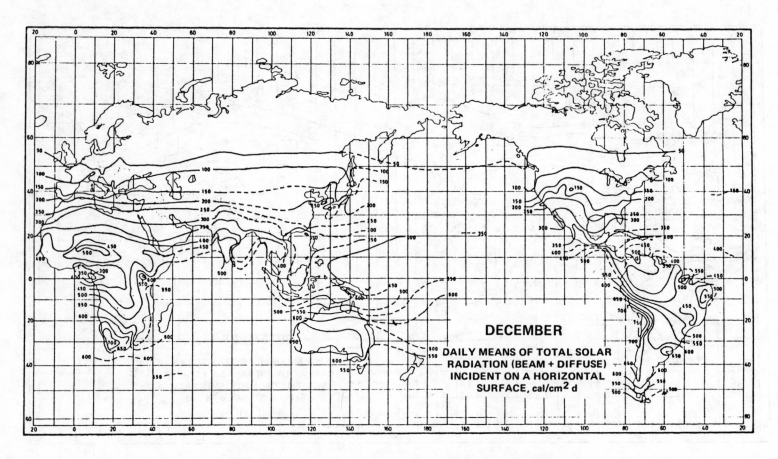

WORLD AVERAGE INSOLATION DATA FOR DECEMBER

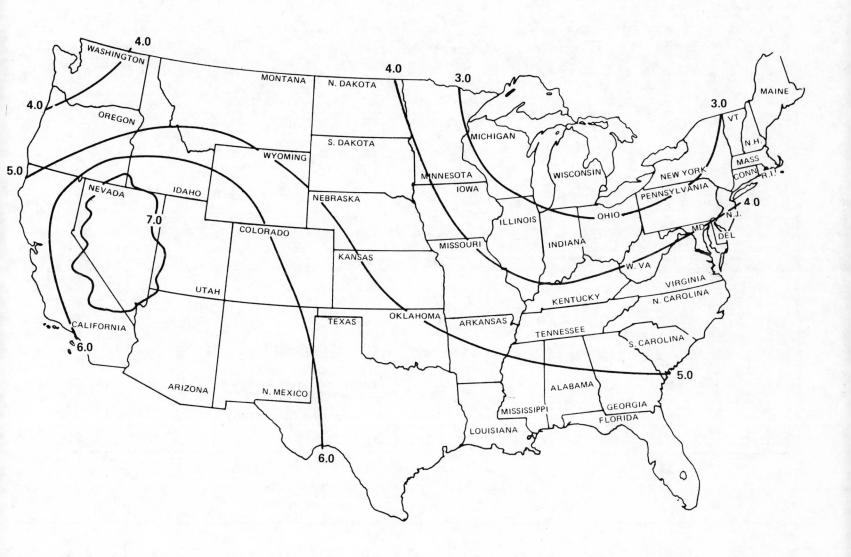

AVERAGE DAILY SOLAR INSOLATION DATA FOR THE UNITED STATES

APPENDIX D
Glossary

APPENDIX D
GLOSSARY

Active Solar:

systems that convert the sun's energy into thermal or electric energy by using some form of force or electrical activity. Photovoltaic, wind, and most solar water heaters are examples of active systems.

Alternating Current:

electrical energy that reverses its direction at regular intervals.

Ambient Temperatures:

temperature of the immediate surrounding environment.

Amp (short for ampere):

the unit strength of a current.

Array:

a number of solar collection devices, usually panels, or modules, arranged in a manner to collect solar energy.

Blocking Diode:

a relatively small semiconductor device, allowing current to flow in only one direction, used in photovoltaic systems to permit the flow of electricity from the photovoltaic array to a battery, but preventing a reverse flow of energy from the batteries to the photovoltaic system, which could damage the system, when the photovoltaic system is not generating electricity.

Cathodic Protection:

a method of slowing down the rate of deterioration in metal pipes, bridges, etc. resulting from a difference in the electrical characteristics of the surrounding ground and metal. A small electric charge is supplied to the metal to be protected.

CdS (Cadmium Sulfide):

a light yellow or orange colored chemical compound produced from cadmium metal in large quantities, used chiefly as a pigment. It can be used in photovoltaic devices to produce electricity from the sun's energy. When acting as a semiconductor, it is always n-type.

Collector:

usually referred to in solar energy as a device that absorbs energy from the sun to convert it into either thermal or electrical energy.

Collector Efficiency:

this is determined by the ratio of energy produced by a solar collector to the radiant energy incident on the collector.

Concentrator:

devices which increase, or "concentrate" the sun's energy on a much smaller surface area. Types of concentrators include parabolic and fresnel lens.

Current:

the rate of flow of an electric charge.

Degree Days:

the sum of the difference between $65^{\circ}F$ ($18.3^{\circ}C$) and the mean daily temperature for each day of the year.

Diffuse Radiation:

the scattered portion of the sun's energy striking the earth's surface. This radiation may be scattered by the atmosphere, moisture in the air, clouds, dust, etc., and is not capable of being focused, as in a concentrating system.

Direct Current:

electrical energy flowing in one direction and of substantially constant value.

Direct Radiation:

this is the portion of the sun's energy that is received on the earth's surface in a narrow angle from the sun's direction and has not been scattered by clouds, dust, water vapor, etc. It is used in concentrating systems.

Discount Rate:

the value of future dollars put in terms of their present worth.

Doping:

the addition of specific materials, or impurities, to a semiconductor in order to alter its electrical properties.

Easement:

legal term referring to a type of interest in real property (not ownership) by someone other than the owner of that property entitling him to specific rights or enjoyments regarding that property.

Efficiency:

in a photovoltaic solar cell, the electrical power output of the solar cell is expressed as a percentage of the amount of solar energy striking it. More generally, the amount of useful energy produced by a system compared to the amount of energy put into it to make it run.

Electrons:

extremely small atomic particles that are negatively charged and are an element of all atoms.

Encapsulant:

material surrounding the solar cell, protecting it from the environment.

Flat-Plate Collector:

a non-concentrating device with a flat surface used to collect solar energy for use as thermal or electrical energy.

GaAs (Gallium Arsenide):

a black chemical compound which in single crystal form has very good properties as a semiconductor turning the sun's energy into electricity. It is being tested for use as a photovoltaic device.

Gigawatt:

1,000 megawatts or 1,000,000,000 watts

Hybrid Systems:

generally means combination of two different renewable energy systems such as PV and wind or PV and thermal (not from the same unit).

Ingot:

conveniently shaped piece of metalic or other material, such as silicon, to be used for further processing such as refining, cutting, or shaping.

Insolation:

the amount of solar radiation received on an area during a set period of time.

Inverter:

a device used to change DC current, which is produced by a photovoltaic system, into AC current which is used in most electrical appliances.

I-V Curve:

a graph of the relationship between current (I) and the voltage (V) of an electrical device such as a solar cell.

Kilowatt:

1,000 watts

Life-cycle Costing:

a method of calculating the total cost or value of an item over its full life time, including interest, maintenance costs, fuel costs, replacement costs, etc. This is usually put in terms of present day dollar value.

Load:

the electrical or heating need that is to be served by a solar or other energy producing device. The load can range from a single device to an entire structure.

Load Profiles:

the amount of energy used by a building or piece of equipment, viewed over time, i.e. an electric oven's load profile may show 1/2 kW hours use in the morning, with no use until early evening when it would peak at 1.5 kW hours and again drop down to 0.

Load Resistance:

the amount of resistance presented by an electric load to the flow of electrical current.

Megawatt:

1,000 kilowatts or 1,000,000 watts.

Milliammeter:

meter which measures milliamps.

Milliampere:

one thousandth of an ampere.

Module:

a number of cells connected together, usually in a "panel," sealed with an encapsulant, and having a standard size and output voltage.

Open Circuit:

where the flow of electricity is prevented through the breaking or opening of the connection or circuit.

Passive Solar System:

a system utilizing components of the building structure itself to provide energy for heating, cooling, and light. These systems have no moving parts, and may include collectors, thermal storage devices, reflectors and other means of collecting and distributing the solar energy. These systems may require significant architectural design features for optimum effectiveness.

Peak Watt:

this unit is used to measure and rate the performance of photovoltaic cells, panels or systems. If a panel were rated at 1 peak watt, it should deliver 1 watt at the specified voltage at a solar irradiation of 10^3 W/m^2, at a specified temperature (usually 28°C) and with respect to it's atmospheric location (usually defined as Air Mass 1.5).

Photovoltaic Generator:

a photovoltaic cell, panel, or system that produces electricity.

Photon:

a unit of energy and visible to us as "light." Specifically, it is a quantum of electromagnetic radiation, the energy E of which is related to the frequency (v) of the radiation by the equation $E = hv$ where h is Planck's constant.

P-N Junction:

the interface surface between the p-type and n-type semiconductor in a photovoltaic cell.

Polycrystalline:

material consisting of many small crystals in a random arrangement.

Power Handling Equipment:

a number of devices, such as inverters, regulators, meters, transformers etc., used to interface between a source of electrical energy, such as a photovoltaic array, and a user of electricity, such as a residence or even a single appliance in order to properly match the electrical output with the electricity needs of the load.

Public Utilities Regulatory Policies Act (PURPA):

an act passed by the U.S. Congress designating certain power production facilities as small power producers (up to 80 MW) and exempting them from many regulatory controls; designating the right of an owner of a photovoltaic system to connect that system into the utility grid; and requiring the utility to purchase power from such systems.

Pyranometer:

instrument for measuring solar radiation at a given location including the direct and diffuse component.

Pyroheliometer:

an instrument that measures only the direct component of solar radiation.

Resistance:

the opposition of a substance to the free flow of electrons or electricity through it.

Retrofitting:

placing solar energy devices on an existing building structure to provide part or all of the energy required by that structure.

Semiconductor:

a class of materials with electrical properties somewhere between those of metals (conductors) and insulators. In photovoltaic cells they absorb photons and emit electrons to produce electricity.

Series Connection:

in a photovoltaic system a set of photovoltaic cells connected one after another whereby the voltage of each cell adds to the other cells thus increasing the output voltage with constant amperage.

Short Circuit:

an abnormal condition in electrical circuits where low resistance exists between two points of different electric potential resulting in a flow of excess current.

Siemens Process:

a method for removing impurities from silicon by using an electric arc.

Silicon:

a non-metallic element, the twentieth in the series of chemical elements, it constitutes more than one quarter of the earth's crust found primarily in sand, but is also combined with other elements and in almost all rocks. In purified forms it acts as a semiconductor and has good properties for use as a photovoltaic device.

Single Crystal:

the perfect state of a solid in which all of the atoms are arranged in an ordered fashion.

Small Power Producer:

as defined in the Public Utilities Regulatory Policies Act it is any power producing facility under 80 megawatts of capacity if the primary source of energy is a renewable resource and the facility is owned by a person who is not primarily engaged in the generation or sale of electric power (other than the sale of electric power from the small power production facility).

Solar Energy:

energy from the sun, usually used for heating or light, specifically, the photon energy originating from the sun's radiation in the wavelength region from 0.3 to 2.7 micrometers.

Solar Energy Research Institute (SERI):

established by the Department of Energy as the headquarters for solar energy research and development coordination efforts. Located in Golden, Colorado.

Solar Envelope:

hypothetical area around a structure used to determine the availability of solar energy to a collector located within the envelope.

Solar Thermal Electric:

solar systems that convert the sun's energy into thermal energy by heating fluids which in turn is used in a more conventional manner to drive turbo-electric generators to produce electricity.

Stand-Alone Systems:

photovoltaic or other power systems not connected to a central utility grid.

Sun Hour or Solar Time:

the hours of the day as determined by the apparent position of the sun (which is rarely the same as local standard time) in any one place. Solar noon is that instant on any day when the sun reaches its maximum altitude for that day.

Sunrights:

a general term referring to an individual's rights with regard to access to the sun's energy. Sunrights vary from place to place depending upon state and local laws.

Terminal Voltage:

the electric potential between any two terminals, i.e. the voltage between the positive and negative terminal of a battery.

Three Mile Island:

location of a nuclear power electric generating station near Harrisburg, Pennsylvania, where the U.S.'s most serious utility nuclear accident occurred on March 28, 1979.

Voltage:

the force with which electrons, are propelled along a path as in a wire.

Voltage Regulator:

an electrical device used to keep voltage at prespecified levels.

Voltmeter:

an instrument used to measure the amount of voltage of an electrical device.

Watt:

equivalent to a current of one ampere under a pressure of one volt. The standard energy equivalent in the U.S. is 1/746 horsepower.

WECS (Wind Energy Conversion System):

a system using rotating blades, rotors, etc. in order to capture the energy contained in the wind for use in generating electricity or pumping water.

ABOUT MONEGON

MONEGON, Ltd., founded in 1979, is a firm organized by leaders in alternative energy technologies in recognition of the need for a private center of excellence in the design, analysis and manufacture of energy systems. MONEGON is dedicated to performing work in a broad range of energy systems with particular emphasis on solar energy technologies and their integration with conventional energy sources.

The firm's capabilities include system design and analysis, system engineering and integration, economic and market analysis, and the manufacture of a variety of solar power systems for home and business use.

MONEGON has two Solar Products Divisions, located in Gaithersburg, Maryland and in Tucson, Arizona. At these facilities, experienced MONEGON engineers and assemblers produce reliable, high quality photovoltaic and solar thermal systems. These low-cost systems include solar hot water collector systems, and photovoltaic water pumps, evaporative coolers, refrigerators, portable AC and DC systems, battery chargers, and other solar power systems. MONEGON also manufactures Solar Total Energy Systems for residential, commercial and industrial use. MONEGON provides a full warranty on all of these products, and can provide full installation and maintenance services.

In addition to solar products and services, MONEGON also publishes a number of studies on solar and other renewable energy technologies. Most of these reports are written for the business and academic communities. One of these publications, entitled "Designing Small Photovoltaic Systems," provides guidance for the photovoltaic system designer. It includes information on design, sizing, and cost estimation procedures, and is available for $10.00.